Electrical Trade Theory

Student's Book

SA Chuturgoon

Electrical Trade Theory N1
Student's Book

21 23 25 27 26 24 22
3 5 7 9 10 8 6 4 2

First edition 2017
Second edition 2021

Published by
Troupant Publishers [Pty] Ltd
PO Box 4532
Northcliff
2115

Distributed by Macmillan South Africa [Pty] Ltd

ISBN: 978-1-4308-0845-9
Web PDF ISBN: 978-1-4308-0846-6

Acknowledgements
Selected images used under licence from Shutterstock.com.

SANS regulations in Modules 6 and 7 reproduced with permission by the South African Bureau of Standards (SABS). Regulations taken from *SANS 10142-1, The wiring of premises Part 1: Low-voltage installations.* South African Bureau of Standards, 2020, Edition 3, ISBN 978-0-626-38495-1

To order any of these books, contact Macmillan Customer Services at:
Tel: (011) 731 3300
Fax: (011) 731 3535
Email: customerservices@macmillaneducation.co.za

Contents

NOTE TO THE STUDENT

The syllabus weighting of the work covered in this textbook is as follows:

Module	Weighting
Safety precautions	10
Fire and firefighting	5
Hand and power tools	5
Direct current (DC) circuit theory	30
Conductors and insulating materials	5
Wiring of premises	25
Testing of a single-phase installation	5
Magnetism and electromagnetism	10
Renewable energy	5
TOTAL	**100**

Safety precautions

Module

1

Overview of Module 1

Safety first! A safe working environment is a productive one. Laws are put in place to ensure the safety of people at work, and to protect equipment and property.

In this module we are going to learn about the Occupational Health and Safety Act (OHS) and safety signage, safety precautions, protective devices and protective equipment used in an electrical working environment.

When you have completed this module, you should be able to:

Unit 1.1: Occupational health and safety

- Explain the purpose of the OHS Act.
- State the duties and/or responsibilities of the employer and employees according to the OHS Act.
- Differentiate between an accident and incident.
- List the causes of accidents/incidents.
- Identify unsafe acts and unsafe conditions in the workplace.

Figure 1.1: Using the correct PPE and working in a safe environment

Unit 1.2: Housekeeping and additional safety precautions

- Define good housekeeping.
- Explain the purpose of housekeeping.
- State the safety precautions to be observed with regards to the following:
    - Machine guarding.
    - Ladders.

Unit 1.3: Signage

- Identify the categories and the colour coding of safety signs.
- Describe the meaning of each sign.

Unit 1.4: Safety switches and protection of electrical installations

- Describe the purpose of the following safety switches:
  - Electrical interlocks.
  - Circuit breakers.
  - Overload relays.
  - Lock-out switches.
  - Earth leakage relays.
- State the procedure to be followed when isolating or locking out a circuit for inspection and repair purposes.

Unit 1.5: Personal protective equipment

- Explain the purpose of the following types of PPE:
  - Hard hats, safety goggles, arc shields, rubber and leather gloves, leather aprons, respirators.

Starter activity

Discuss the following in class:

- Electricity is our most useful form of energy, but also very dangerous. Why do you think that we do not often hear of people being shocked by electricity?
- You will soon be working in a factory or a workshop. List all the safety measures that you will take to ensure your personal safety and the safety of others.
- Every time you open the door of a working microwave oven, it automatically switches off. How do you think this is made possible?

Unit 1.1: Occupational health and safety

Definition of safety

Safety is a condition of being protected from danger, risk or harm, or being unlikely to cause danger, risk or harm.

It is very important that all people in the workplace work safely and that employers create a safe working environment. A safe environment reduces man-hours lost because of injury to a person, damage to equipment and downtime of machinery.

Accidents and illness in the workplace not only interfere with the flow of work, but also cause pain and suffering to the injured and sick, as well as their families.

1.1.1 The Occupational Health and Safety (OHS) Act 85/93

The South African government passed the OHS Act in 1993 to help prevent work-related injuries and illness.

Purpose of the OHS Act

According to its opening paragraph, the OHS Act was designed for these reasons:

Purpose of the Occupation Health and Safety Act 85 of 1993

"To provide for the health and safety of persons at work and the persons in connection with the use of ***plant*** and machinery; the protection of persons other than persons at work against ***hazards*** to health and safety arising out of or in connection with the activities of persons at work."

plant: *a building where goods are manufactured by machines*

hazard: *source of exposure to danger*

See it online 

OHS Act
You can download the full OHS Act from the South African government website | https://www.gov.za/documents/occupational-health-and-safety-act

Legal duties and/or responsibilities of the employer and employee

Who is an employer?

Definition of employer

Any person, company, partnership or non-profit organisation that employs one or more employees is an employer.

Duties of an employer

All employers are legally bound to provide and maintain a working environment that is safe and free of risks to health. The Act requires of employers to, as far as is reasonably practicable:

- Provide and maintain a safe plant.
- Provide and maintain safe systems of work – for example controlling entry to high-risk areas and providing systems to prevent falls from heights.
- Ensure the safe use, handling, storage or transport of plant or substances.
- Keep workplaces safe and free of risks to health.
- Provide suitable facilities for welfare at the workplace.
- Give employees the necessary information, instruction, training or supervision to enable them to do their work in a way that is safe and without risk to health.

Who is an employee?

Definition of employee

Any person having a contract of employment or contract of training is an employee.

Volunteers are not employees and independent contractors may be employees.

Duties of an employee

As an employee, your duties in terms of the OHS Act are:

- To take reasonable care for your health and safety in the workplace and to take reasonable care for the health and safety of others who may be affected by what you do or don't do.
- To cooperate with your employer about any action he or she takes to comply with the OHS Act or Regulations – for example to use equipment properly, follow safe work policies and procedures, and attend training.
- To not intentionally or recklessly interfere with or misuse anything at the workplace that is there to support health, safety and welfare.

1.1.2 Accidents and incidents

The terms 'accidents', 'near misses' and 'incidents' are commonly used when talking about health and safety. There are varying interpretations of these concepts, which can become very confusing.

Accidents
Learn more about the causes of accidents in this video – Accidents – Six Main Causes by RS SafetyTV | https://youtu.be/VEACNeNynBg

Let us try to understand the difference between them by considering their effects with regard to injury and damage to property:

Definition of accidents, incidents and near misses

- An **accident** is an undesired and unplanned event that results in personal injury and/or damage to property and/or business interruption.
- A **near miss** is an undesired and unplanned event that does not result in personal injury, but may result in damage to property and/or business interruption.
- An **incident** is something that happened, an event or occurrence.

Therefore, an incident could be an accident with personal injury and damage to property, or a near miss, with no personal injury but with a possibility of damage to property. Incidents range in severity from near misses to fatal accidents.

Causes of incidents

Incidents often result from unsafe acts and unsafe conditions (see section 1.1.3). They can be caused by either personal or job factors:

Personal factors

- Lack of knowledge and/or skill.
- Physical or mental inability.
- Improper attitude or motivation.
- Unsafe acts.

Job factors

- Unsafe conditions and physical environment (see section 1.1.3).
- Inadequate work standards.

1.1.3 Unsafe acts and unsafe conditions

Unsafe acts and unsafe conditions can lead to incidents and accidents in the workplace and they must be avoided.

Unsafe acts

Definition of unsafe act

An unsafe act is any act that is not performed according to prescribed safety standards or practice.

Unsafe acts by people can be described as follows:

- Working at unsafe speeds.
- Working without authority.
- Failure to secure machinery and workpieces.
- Making safety devices inoperative.
- Arranging or placing objects unsafely.
- Fooling, teasing and abusing workmates.
- Using equipment unsafely.
- Taking chances.
- Failure to use safety equipment or to wear protective clothing.

Unsafe conditions

Definition of unsafe condition

An unsafe condition is any deviation from accepted safety standards which, if not rectified, may be the cause of accidents resulting in injury and/or damage.

The following are regarded as unsafe conditions:

- Unsafe construction.
- Disorderly and haphazard planning.
- Lack of machine and other guards.
- Inadequate ventilation.
- Unsafe lighting.
- Unsafe storage of hazardous materials.
- Overcrowding in workshops.
- No personal protective equipment.
- Poor factory layout with inadequate or poorly marked walkways.

Activity 1.1

1. What is safety? (4)
2. State the purpose of the OHS Act. (5)
3. Who is an employer? (4)
4. State five legal duties and/or responsibilities of the employer as contained in the OHS Act. (5)
5. Explain the difference between an accident and a near miss. (7)
6. State five causes of accidents/incidents. (5)
7. State five unsafe acts that could lead to accidents. (5)
8. State five unsafe conditions that could lead to accidents. (5)

TOTAL: [40]

Unit 1.2: Housekeeping and additional safety precautions

1.2.1 Good housekeeping

Definition of good plant housekeeping

Good plant housekeeping means to have 'a place for everything and everything in its place' at all times.

Purpose of housekeeping

The purpose of housekeeping is to ensure that the plant is neat, orderly, ***sanitary*** and safe (free of hazards).

sanitary: *clean and hygienic*

Good plant housekeeping is desirable and important because:

- It saves time spent on looking for goods, tools and articles.
- Space is saved when everything is stacked away tidily.
- Injuries are avoided when gangways and working areas are kept clear of surplus materials.

Figure 1.2: Good plant housekeeping

Figure 1.3: Poor housekeeping

- Fire hazards are reduced if combustible materials are kept in proper containers.
- It improves the working environment.
- It improves efficiency and production.

Disadvantages of poor housekeeping

- People tripping over loose objects on floors.
- Objects falling from above.
- People slipping on greasy, wet or dirty floors.
- People bumping against poorly piled or badly placed materials.
- Fires.
- Injury because of protruding nails, splinters, etc.

1.2.2 Plant safety precautions

Safety requires workers to always be aware of their workplace surroundings and the equipment and machinery in this space. Tools and machines can present safety hazards. Workers must be fully trained in using all equipment and in taking the relevant safety precautions before they use it.

Machine guarding

Definition of machine guard

A machine guard is a protective device (shield, barrier or other protective system) that protects users from the hazardous parts of a machine.

Machine guarding is essential because injuries caused by rotating parts of machines are usually severe and permanent. These injuries are preventable in most cases.

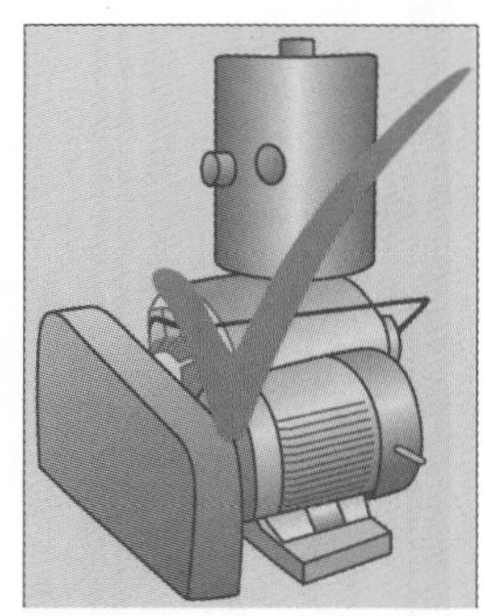

Figure 1.4: Machine guarding

There are two classes of machine guards:

- Transmission guards (guards for pulleys, gears and shafts).
- Point of operation guards (guards covering circular saw blades, guillotine knives, punch press dies).

We can also divide guards into three basic types:

Table 1.1: Three basic types of guards

Type	Function
Fixed guards	This type is used especially on ***transmission machinery*** and does not move with each operation.
Interlocking guards	This type prevents the operation of the controls which set the machine in motion until the guard is moved into place.
Automatic guards	This type prevents the operator from coming into contact with dangerous parts of a machine while it is operating.

transmission machine: *a machine that uses gears to transfer energy*

Characteristics of a good machine guard

A good machine guard should:

- Provide maximum positive protection.
- Block access to the danger zone during operation.
- Be a permanent part of the machine without affecting its structure.
- Not affect efficient operation of the machine.
- Be strong enough to withstand normal wear and tear.
- Be corrosion and fire resistant.
- Be easily replaceable.

Safe use of ladders

Working with ladders can be dangerous. The following are safety precautions to be observed when working with ladders:

- Always avoid bringing the ladder in contact with electricity.
- Unless the ladder is securely tied at the top, it should always be held in position by another person while in use.

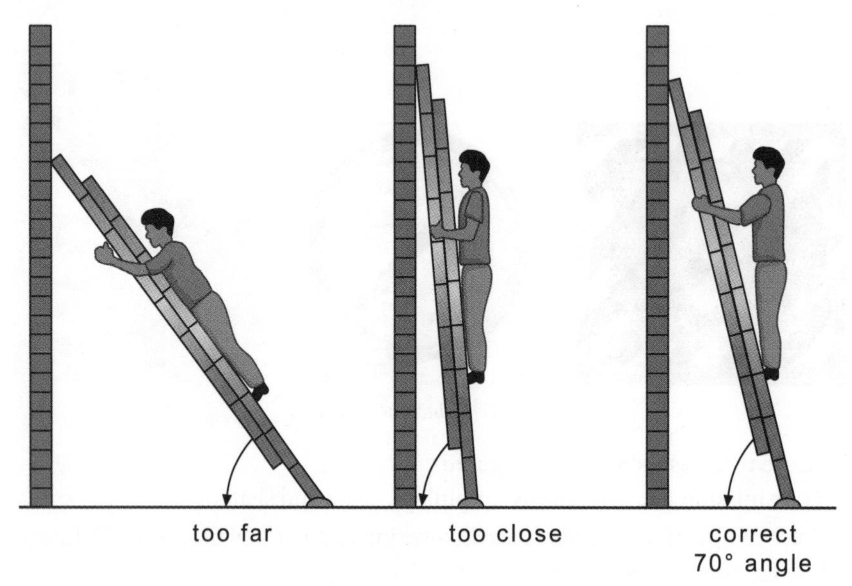

Figure 1.5: Safe use of a ladder

- Wherever possible, an extendable ladder should extend 1 m above its support.
- Ladders should be inspected frequently and defective ladders should be repaired or replaced.
- Wooden ladders must not be painted, because paint hides cracks.
- Do not use ladders horizontally as walkways or as scaffolding.
- Do not leave a ladder where it may fall.
- Do not place a ladder in front of a doorway unless you have taken adequate precautions.
- Ensure that the ladder is equipped with safety feet.
- Use the correct ladder for the job.

Safety precautions in a workshop

The following general precautions should be observed at all times in a workshop to keep it safe:

horseplay: *rough play; fooling around*

apparel: *covering for the human body; clothing*

- No ***horseplay*** is allowed.
- Always maintain good housekeeping.
- Ensure that the workshop is well ventilated and well lit.
- Walkways must be clearly marked.
- Obey all safety signs.
- Use the appropriate personal protective equipment.
- Store gas cylinders in a cool place and away from open flames and sparks.
- Always tie up long hair when drilling, grinding, etc.
- Always wear the correct protective ***apparel*** when working with dangerous chemicals.
- Always wear the correct protective apparel when welding.

Activity 1.2

1.	What do you understand by good plant housekeeping?	(3)
2.	State four advantages of good plant housekeeping.	(4)
3.	State the purpose of machine guarding.	(3)
4.	Name the two classes of machine guards and give two examples of each.	(6)
5.	State five characteristics of a good machine guard.	(5)
6.	State four safety precautions to be observed when working with ladders.	(4)
7.	State five safety precautions to be observed in a workshop.	(5)
		TOTAL: [30]

Unit 1.3: Signage

Signage is used to provide important information and safety guidelines, and to identify hazards in the workplace.

1.3.1 Colour coding

Identifying machinery and different machine parts with colour codes helps people to recognise them quickly. Colour codes also warn against danger, thus reducing industrial accidents.

Colour schemes should be the same throughout the factory (plant). Colour coding helps workers to react correctly in the case of emergencies, provided they are trained to understand the colour-coding system.

1.3.2 Symbolic safety signs

Definition of symbolic safety sign

Symbolic safety signs are a type of sign that uses shape, colour and pictograms. They are displayed to ensure the safety of employees and visitors in a workplace.

The purpose of safety signs is to:

- Warn against hazards.
- Prohibit certain objects or behaviour.
- Indicate compulsory actions such as the required use of PPE.
- Identify the location of exits and safety equipment.

The advantage of symbolic safety signs is that they can be instantly recognised and understood by all language groups, and regardless of degree of literacy.

The South African Bureau of Standards (SABS), in conjunction with the National Occupational Safety Association (NOSA) and other representatives from industry, has laid down set standards for symbolic safety signs in South Africa.

A symbolic safety sign consists of the following three parts:

- A geometric shape.
- A colour.
- A pictogram (picture).

See it online 

SABS

Learn more about the South African Bureau of Standards (SABS) on their website | https://www.sabs.co.za/ . Standards such as the Wiring Code (SANS 10142-1) can be purchased from this site.

Table 1.2: Symbolic safety signs

Type	Geometric shape	Colour	Examples
Warning	Triangle	Yellow background Black picture Black border	• Live electrical conductors. • Poisonous substances. • Low headroom owing to structures. • Handrails. • Change in floor levels or other tripping hazards.
Prohibitory	Circle with diagonal line	White background Black picture Red border Red diagonal line Exception: The 'no entry' sign is a white horizontal line on a red background.	• No smoking. • No photography. • No unauthorised entry. • No cellphones. • Do not touch.
Mandatory (Compulsory)	Circle	Blue background White picture	• Mind your head. • Wear gloves. • Wear protective clothing. • Use dustbins. • Wear goggles. • Put on gumboots.
Informatory (General)	Square or rectangle EMERGENCY ASSEMBLY POINT	Green background White picture	• Exit signs. • Fire assembly point. • Location of first aid. • Emergency showers. • Location of gas masks. • Fire exit.
Informatory (Fire equipment)	Square or rectangle	White background Red picture Red border	• Location of fire extinguishers. • Location of fire hoses. • Location of fire hydrants.

Activity 1.3

1. State two advantages of colour coding machinery and machine parts. (2)
2. State the purpose of symbolic safety signs. (4)
3. List the three parts of a symbolic safety sign. (3)
4. List five types of symbolic safety signs. (5)
5. Name the colours that you would find on the following signs:
   - 5.1 Warning. (2)
   - 5.2 Prohibitory. (3)
6. Give two examples of each of the following safety signs:
   - 6.1 Informatory (general).
   - 6.2 Warning.
   - 6.3 Prohibitory. (3 × 2 = 6)

TOTAL: [25]

Unit 1.4: Safety switches and protection of electrical installations

Electricity is our most useful form of energy, but also extremely dangerous. Extreme care must be taken to ensure that no accidents will occur because of carelessness or negligence.

Electrical equipment and ***installations*** must be protected against the harmful effects of fault currents. It must also be possible to isolate them so that inspection, repairs and maintenance can be carried out.

installation (electrical): *an assembly of electrical wiring, electrical components and outlets in a residential, commercial or industrial setting*

elecrocute: *injure or kill by electric shock*

disconnector: *a switch (or off-load **isolator**) used to open or break a circuit by disconnecting it from its energy supply only after the current has been interrupted by some other means*

isolator: *device used for isolating a circuit or equipment from a source of power*

lock-out switch: *manually operated disconnector with a locking facility*

1.4.1 Isolation for inspection and repairs

To safely carry out repairs and maintenance on electrical equipment and circuits, correct isolating procedures must be followed.

> **Definition of isolation or 'locking out'**
>
> To isolate, in electrical terms, means to open or break a circuit so that it is not electrically continuous (i.e. so that current cannot flow).

The purpose of isolating (also called 'locking out') is to prevent workers who are doing repairs or maintenance from getting ***electrocuted*** when an unauthorised person switches on the electricity.

Lock-out switches

Electrical installations are fitted with ***disconnectors*** that allow the electrical circuits to be isolated for repairs and maintenance. A ***lock-out switch*** is a disconnector that is manually operated and has a locking facility which allows it to be locked in the 'off' position. This is to prevent any unauthorised people from switching on the circuit.

The following simple procedure should be followed when isolating a circuit for inspection, maintenance and repairs to be carried out:

earth: *to discharge electrical energy directly into the ground*

gang lock: *a locking mechanism that allows many people to use their own padlocks to lock the mechanism; the locking mechanism can be removed only after each person has removed his or her padlock*

busbar: *an electrical conductor, capable of carrying a high current, usually used to make a common connection between several circuits in a system*

bar: *prevent or prohibit*

Step 1	Notify all persons who will be affected by the switch-off.
Step 2	Switch off the main disconnector.
Step 3	Lock the main disconnector in the 'off' (open) position. The key to the lock must be kept with the electrician in charge.
Step 4	As a means of extra precaution, make sure that one of the three phases on the load side of the main disconnector is ***earthed***.
Step 5	Display a danger sign near the main disconnector.
Step 6	Finally, test for power before commencing work.

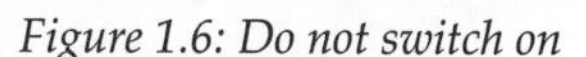
Figure 1.6: Do not switch on

Figure 1.7: Live conductors

Important

A ***gang lock*** (see Figure 1.8) must be used when two or more crews work on the isolated section. Each crew leader must lock the gang lock and keep the key.

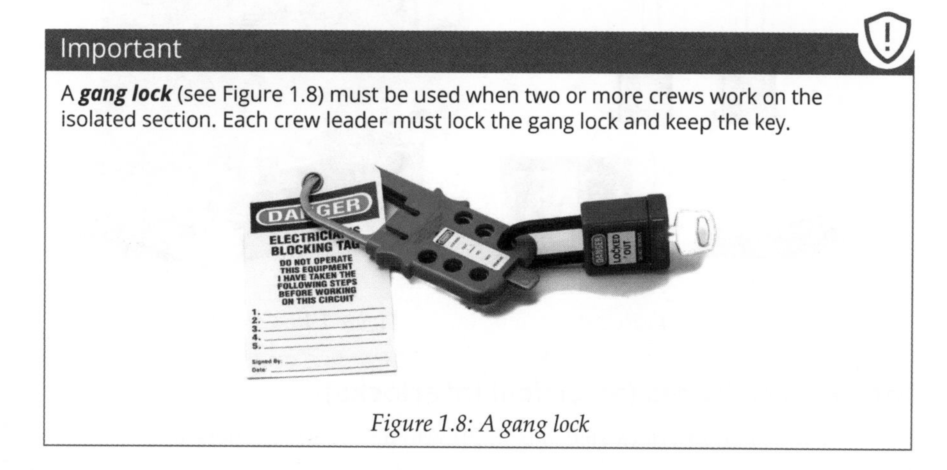

Figure 1.8: A gang lock

1.4.2 Barring entry where there are live conductors

For reasons of safety, no unauthorised person shall enter a venue such as a meter room or substation where there are exposed live conductors such as ***busbars***.

The venue must be kept locked at all times and a danger sign must be clearly displayed.

1.4.3 Safety switches

> **Definition of safety switch**
> Safety switches are protective devices used to protect electrical equipment from damage due to electrical faults and people from injury.

We learned about one type of safety switch – a lock-out switch – in section 1.4.1. Now we will learn about more commonly used safety switches.

Circuit breakers and fuses

Fuses and ***circuit breakers*** are used to protect electrical installations against the harmful effects of ***overcurrents*** caused by ***overloads*** and ***short circuits***.

These protective devices are expected to do the following:

- **In the event of an overload:**
  Automatically disconnect the load from the supply but allowing a little time delay.
- **In the event of a short circuit:**
  Automatically and instantly disconnect the load from the supply.

fuse: *safety device in an electric plug or circuit containing a thin wire that melts and breaks to stop the flow of current in case of a fault; cannot be reused*

circuit breaker: *a protective switch that automatically interrupts current flow in the event of an overload or short circuit; can be reset and reused*

overcurrent: *any current greater than that intended for the conductor*

overload: *a fault condition that occurs when the circuit is expected to carry more current than it was designed for*

short circuit: *a fault condition that occurs when an abnormal connection allows current to flow through an unintended path that has no or very little resistance*

interlock switch: *switch used to prevent an incorrect operation by interrupting or diverting current flow from one conductor to another*

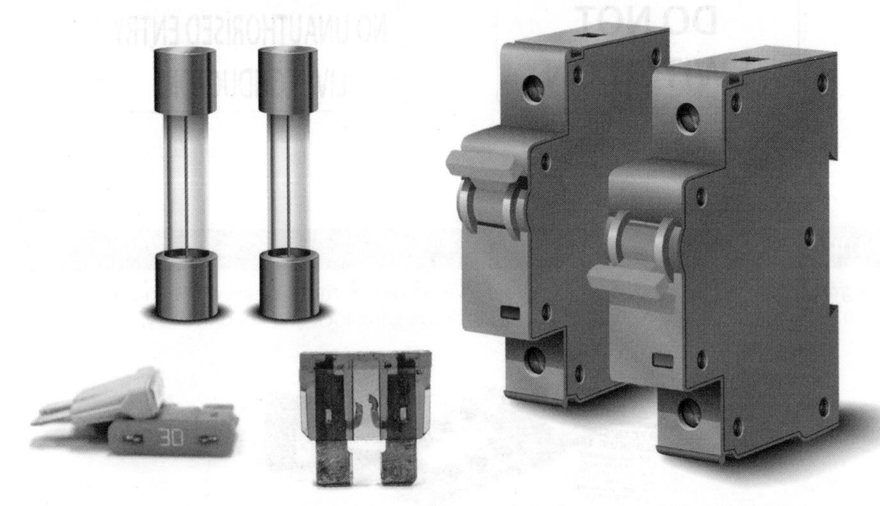

Figure 1.9: Fuses *Figure 1.10: Circuit breakers*

> Note
> You will learn more about protection from overcurrents, fuses and circuit breakers in Module 6, section 6.2.3.

Interlock switches (electrical interlocks)

The function of an ***interlock switch*** is to prevent an incorrect operation from taking place.

This type of switch disconnects certain components from the power supply if a machine is opened to prevent injury. For example, an interlock switch will prevent a microwave oven from switching on unless the door is closed. Likewise, this switch will not allow a lift or a washing machine to operate while the door is open.

Figure 1.11: Interlock switch

Overload relay

overload relay: *a protective device used in motor circuits to automatically disconnect the motor from the supply in the event of any overcurrent*

motor: *a machine that uses electricity or fuel to produce movement*

earth leakage relay (ELR): *a protective device used to automatically disconnect an installation from the supply in the event of the leakage current exceeding a certain predetermined value*

leakage current: *electric current that has crossed a boundary normally viewed as insulation*

Overload relays are protective devices used in the circuits of ***motors*** to automatically disconnect the motor from the supply in the event of an overcurrent. See Figure 1.12.

Earth leakage relay

The function of an ***earth leakage relay (ELR)*** is to automatically disconnect an installation from the supply if a ***leakage current*** exceeds a certain predetermined value. See Figure 1.13.

Note

You will learn more about protection from leakage currents and earth leakage relays in Module 6, section 6.2.1.

Figure 1.12: An overload relay

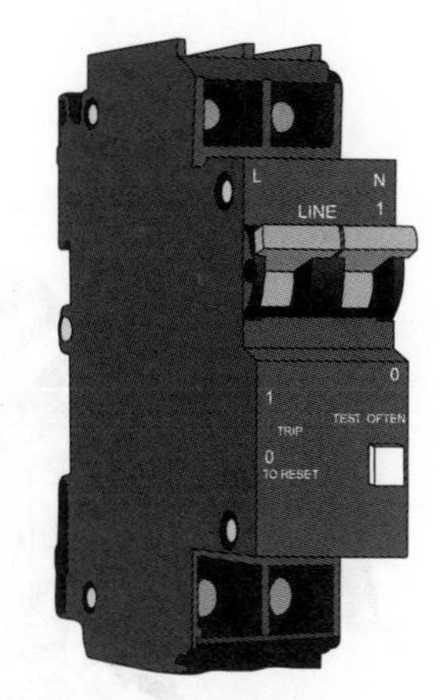

Figure 1.13: A single-phase ELR

Activity 1.4

1. What is the purpose of isolating an electric circuit? (4)
2. State six simple steps to be followed when isolating a circuit for inspection and repairs to be carried out. (6)
3. What do you understand by 'locking out entry where there are live conductors'? (4)
4. State three reasons why electrical circuits will have to be isolated. (3)
5. State the function of fuses and circuit breakers. (4)
6. State the function of an interlock switch. (2)
7. State the function of an earth leakage relay. (4)
8. State the function of an overload relay. (3)

TOTAL: [30]

Unit 1.5: Personal protective equipment

Definition of personal protective equipment (PPE)

Personal protective equipment refers to any clothing and equipment intended to protect a worker's body from injury or infection.

PPE includes hard hats, goggles and any other clothing intended to protect the worker's body from injury or infection. By law the employer has to provide the employee with all relevant PPE.

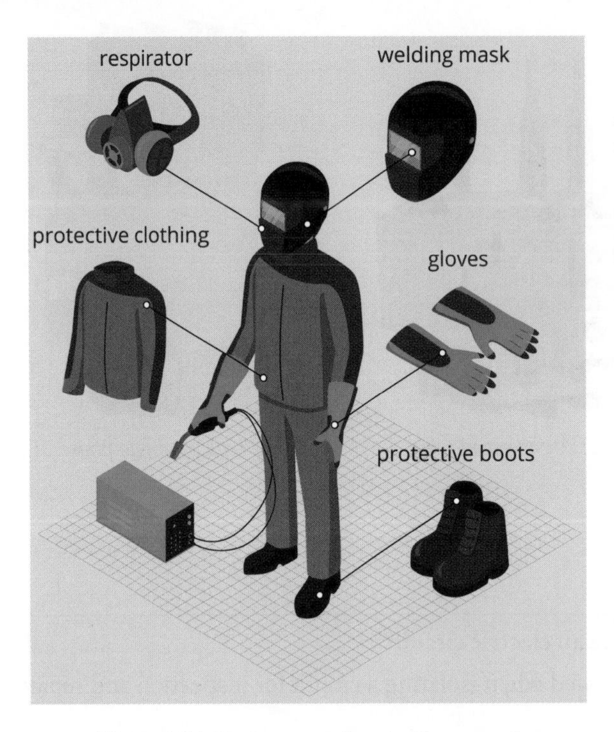

Figure 1.14: Basic personal protective apparel

1.5.1 Head protection

Hard hats are used to prevent injury to the head caused by sharp or falling objects.

Figure 1.15: A hard hat as protection

Figure 1.16: An arc shield (welding helmet)

1.5.2 Eye and face protection

Eye and face protection must be used when welding, drilling, grinding, cutting, gas brazing or working with dangerous chemicals.

- **Clear anti-scratch safety goggles** are the most common type of eye and face protection.
- **Darkened safety goggles** are to be used when gas brazing or using a cutting torch.
- **Special welding helmets (*arc shields*)** must be worn when welding (see Figure 1.16). Failure to do so will result in 'arc eyes', which is extremely painful. Arc eyes, or welder's flash, is an inflammation of the cornea caused by exposure to ultraviolet radiation during welding.

arc shield: *protective welding helmet*

respiratory system: *organs in the body that allow a person to breath*

1.5.3 Respiratory protective equipment

The function of this safety apparel is to protect the ***respiratory system*** against the harmful effects of dust and fumes. Dust masks or respirators can be used (see Figure 1.17).

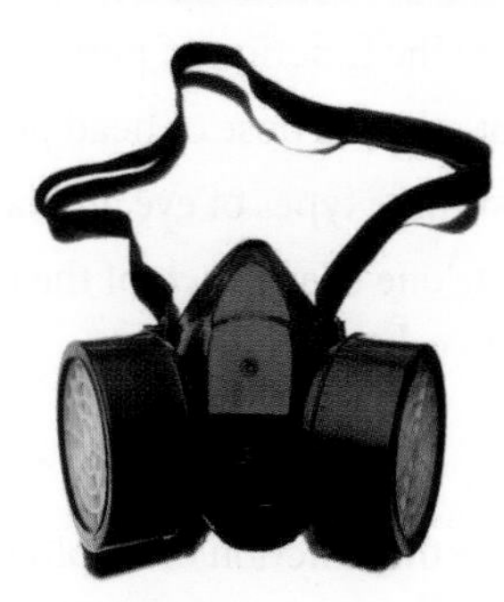

Figure 1.17: A dust mask and respirator

1.5.4 Hand protection

The following types of hand protection are available:

- **Leather gloves:** Must be worn when working with hot or sharp objects.
- **Rubber gloves:** Must be worn when working with dangerous chemicals such as acids.
- **Insulated gloves:** These are special gloves designed to protect against electrocution while working with live conductors.

1.5.5 Body protection

The worker's body needs to be covered sufficiently to protect it from chemicals, heat, sparks, etc. Workers should wear thick long-sleeved jackets and thick long pants without turn-ups. The legs of the pants must overlap the tops of the worker's boots. Full overalls can also be worn. Clothing should be free of oil and grease.

Aprons are also essential. The following types of aprons are available:

- **Rubber aprons:** Must be worn when working with dangerous chemicals such as acids.
- **Leather aprons:** Must be worn when welding, grinding or gas cutting.

1.5.6 Foot protection

Special safety boots should be worn at all times.

- Safety-toed shoes are used to protect the worker's feet against injury from falling and sharp objects.
- The soles of the boots should ideally have good traction to protect the worker from slips and falls.
- Depending on the requirements of the trade, boots may be made from leather, rubber or insulating materials to ensure that they are heat resistant, chemical resistant or non-conductive as required.

Activity 1.5

1. State the function of personal protective equipment. (3)
2. State the purpose of head protection. (3)
3. List three types of eye and face protection and state when each one must be used. (6)
4. State one use of each of the following:
   4.1 Leather gloves.
   4.2 Rubber gloves.
   4.3 Insulated gloves. $(3 \times 1 = 3)$
5. State the function of respiratory protective equipment. (3)
6. State the type of apron to be used when:
   6.1 Working with dangerous chemicals.
   6.2 Welding. $(2 \times 1 = 2)$

TOTAL: [20]

Summary of Module 1

We have covered the following in this module. See if you have mastered each of these sections.

Unit 1.1 Occupational health and safety

- Safety is the condition of being protected from danger, risks or harm, or being unlikely to cause danger, risks or harm.
- The South African government passed the OHS Act in 1993 to help prevent work-related injuries and illness.
- Accidents and illness that occur in the workplace not only interfere with the flow of work, but also cause pain and suffering to the injured and sick, as well as their families.
- Any person, company, partnership or non-profit organisation that employs one or more employees is an employer.
- Any person having a contract of employment or contract of training is an employee.
- An accident is an undesired and unplanned event that results in personal injury and/or damage to property and/or business interruption.
- A near miss is an undesired and unplanned event that does not result in personal injury, but may result in damage to property and/or business interruption.
- An incident is something that happened, an event or occurrence. Therefore, an incident could be an accident with personal injury and damage to property or a near miss with no personal injury but with a possibility of damage to property.
- Accidents/incidents can be caused by personal factors or job factors.

Unit 1.2 Housekeeping and additional safety precautions

- Plant housekeeping means to have 'a place for everything and everything in its place' at all times.
- Machine guarding is essential because injuries caused by rotating parts of machines are usually severe and permanent.
- There are different classes and basic types of machine guards.

Unit 1.3 Signage

- Identifying machinery and different machine parts with colour codes helps people to recognise them quickly. Colour codes also warn against danger, thus reducing industrial accidents.
- Colour coding helps workers to react correctly in the case of emergencies, provided they are trained to understand the colour-coding system.
- Symbolic safety signs are a type of sign that uses shape, colour and pictograms. They are displayed to ensure the safety of employees and visitors in a workplace.
- The purpose of safety signs is to warn against hazards, prohibit certain objects or behaviour, indicate compulsory actions such as the required use of PPE and identify the location of exits and safety equipment.
- The advantage of symbolic safety signs is that they can be instantly recognised and understood by all language groups, and regardless of degree of literacy.

Unit 1.4 Safety switches and protection of electrical installations

- To isolate, in electrical terms, means to open or break a circuit so that it is not electrically continuous.
- The purpose of isolating is to prevent workers who are doing repairs or maintenance from getting electrocuted when an unauthorised person switches on the electricity.
- A gang lock must be used when two or more crews work on the isolated section. Each crew leader must lock the gang lock and keep the key.
- A lock-out switch is a disconnector that is manually operated and has a locking facility which allows it to be locked in the 'off' position to prevent any unauthorised people from switching on the circuit.
- For reasons of safety, no unauthorised person shall enter a venue such as a meter room or substation where there are exposed live conductors such as busbars. The venue must be kept locked at all times and a danger sign must be clearly displayed.
- Fuses and circuit breakers are used to protect electrical installations against the harmful effects of overcurrents caused by overloads and short circuits.
- An interlock switch is used to prevent an incorrect operation from taking place.
- An earth leakage relay is used to automatically disconnect an installation from the supply if a leakage current exceeds a certain predetermined value.
- Overload relays are protective devices used in the circuits of motors to automatically disconnect the motor from the supply in the event of an overcurrent.

Unit 1.5 Personal protective equipment

- Personal protective equipment is used to protect the worker's body from injury or infection.
- Hard hats are used to prevent injury to the head caused by sharp or falling objects.
- Eye and face protection must be used when welding, drilling, grinding, cutting, gas brazing or working with dangerous chemicals.
- Respiratory protective equipment is used to protect the respiratory system against the harmful effects of dust and fumes.
- Safety boots should be worn at all times to protect the worker's feet from sharp or falling objects and from heat, electricity and chemicals.

Summative assessment for Module 1

1. In engineering terms, what is a plant? (3)
2. Who is an employee? (3)
3. State four legal duties and/or responsibilities of the employee as contained in the OHS Act. (4)
4. Explain what is meant by an incident. (5)
5. State five disadvantages of poor housekeeping. (5)
6. List three basic types of guards and state the function of each. (3)
7. Name the colours that you would find on the following signs:
   - 7.1 Mandatory (compulsory).
   - 7.2 Informatory (fire equipment). $(2 \times 2 = 4)$
8. Give two examples of each of the following safety signs:
   - 8.1 Mandatory (compulsory).
   - 8.2 Informatory (fire equipment). $(2 \times 2 = 4)$
9. In electrical terms, what does 'isolate' mean? (3)
10. State two requirements with regard to venues that have live conductors. (2)
11. State what fuses and circuit breakers are expected to do in the event of:
    - 11.1 An overload.
    - 11.2 A short circuit. $(2 \times 2 = 4)$
12. Name two appliances whose functioning is dependent on interlock switches. (2)
13. Whose responsibility is it to provide PPE? (1)
14. List four types of jobs that require the use of eye and face protection. (4)
15. Name the type of respiratory protective equipment to be used when:
    - 15.1 Working in dusty areas. (2)
    - 15.2 Working with chemicals. (1)

TOTAL: [50]

Module

2 Fire and firefighting

Overview of Module 2

Fires can be very destructive to people, plant and equipment. Basic firefighting knowledge is essential in any working environment.

In this module we are going to learn about how fires are started, classes of fire, types of fire extinguishers and how to respond if a fire breaks out in the workplace.

When you have completed this module, you should be able to:

Unit 2.1: Fire and firefighting

- State the cause of fire.
- Describe the different classes of fire.
- State the safety precautions to be observed while fighting a fire.
- Identify the different fire extinguishers for the different classes of fire.

Figure 2.1: Extinguishing a Class A fire

Starter activity

Discuss the following in class:

- Fires are very dangerous and destructive. What do you think are some of the common causes of fires in any place of work?
- A fire has started in an office block where there is a lot of electronic equipment. Do you think that it would be a wise idea to use water to put out the fire?
- What are the different types of fire extinguishers available?

Unit 2.1: Fire and firefighting

extinguish: *put an end to; put out*

combustible: *able to burn easily*

ignite: *catch fire*

Firefighting is the act of attempting to ***extinguish*** unwanted fires and prevent them from spreading. An understanding of the causes of fire and the classes of fire is essential to prevent and combat them. It is also important to understand how to fight them safely.

2.1.1 The fire triangle

Definition of fire

A fire is a process that occurs when a ***combustible*** material combines chemically with oxygen in the air and extreme heat, and gives off bright light, heat and smoke.

The fire triangle shown in Figure 2.2 is a simple model which helps us understand the ingredients needed for a fire to start and be sustained:

- Heat (source of ***ignition***).
- Fuel (some sort of combustible material).
- Oxygen.

Figure 2.2: The fire triangle

2.1.2 Causes of fire (heat)

The causes of fire or sources of heat/ignition are:

- Electrical faults.
- Open flames.
- Heated surfaces.
- Matches and cigarettes.
- Spontaneous reactions.
- Static electricity.
- Friction.
- Lightning.

2.1.3 Classes of fire and fire extinguishers

The type of fuel that contributes to the fire determines the class of fire and the type of fire extinguisher that can be used to put an end to the fire.

> **Definition of fire extinguisher**
>
> A fire extinguisher is a portable device that sprays water, foam, gas or other chemicals to extinguish small fires.

Figure 2.3: A fire extinguisher

We have seen that all three elements of the fire triangle are necessary to sustain a fire. The function of a fire extinguisher is to remove *at least one* of the elements of a fire in order to put out the fire.

Table 2.1 shows the different classes of fires, the types of fuel (combustibles) present and the appropriate fire extinguishers to be used.

Table 2.1: Classes of fire and fire extinguishers

Class	Type of fuel	Type of extinguisher
A	Wood, paper, coal, grass, tobacco, cloth and other organic materials	Water, foam, dry powder and wet chemicals
B	Flammable liquids and greases, e.g. alcohol, benzene, petrol, oil, paraffin	Carbon dioxide, dry powder, foam
C	Fires occurring in the presence of live electrical installations	Carbon dioxide, dry powder
D	Fires occurring because of combustible metals, e.g. magnesium, sodium, potassium and titanium	Dry powder
K	Fires occurring because of vegetable oils, animal oils or fats in cooking appliances	Wet chemical

Important 

- There is much confusion surrounding fire classes. Different countries use different classes for different fuels.
- We are going to use the fire classes as stipulated in the South African National Standards (SANS 10400-7: 2011).

How to use a fire extinguisher

mnemonic: *memory aid*

In order to use a fire extinguisher correctly, remember the PASS ***mnemonic***:

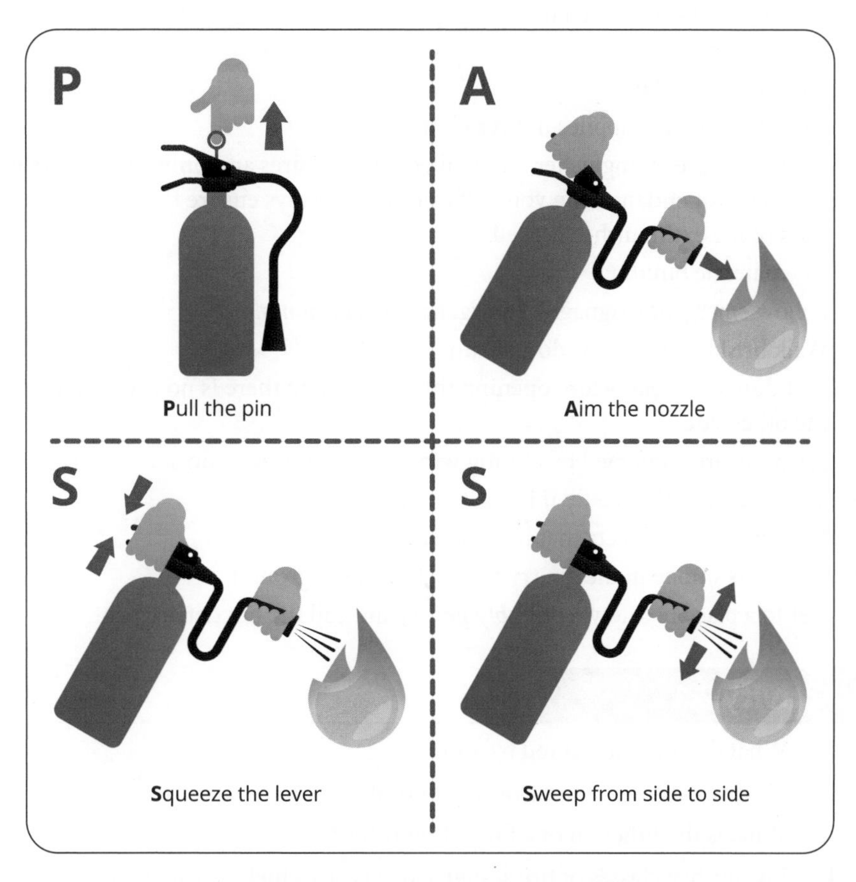

Figure 2.4: Correct use of a fire extinguisher

See it online

Fire extinguishers

Learn how to use a fire extinguisher in this video – How to Use a Fire Extinguisher by Howcast | https://youtu.be/lUojO1HvC8c

2.1.4 The dangers of fire

Fires are very dangerous because:

- Fires spread very fast (you will have very little time to escape or help others to escape).
- Fires generate lots of heat (this heat can kill people or if superheated air is inhaled, it can damage the lungs; fire will also burn the skin).
- Fires are dark (the thick black smoke given off by fires seriously limits visibility).
- Fires are deadly (deaths are caused by burns or when the thick black smoke and toxic fumes are inhaled).

2.1.5 Safety precautions when fighting a fire

Because fires are so dangerous, it is very important to follow these safety precautions in the event of a fire:

- Do not panic.
- Sound the fire alarm.
- Switch off power supplies if it is safe to do so.
- Only use a fire extinguisher for small, contained fires and only when there is no chance of endangering yourself or others. Always ensure that the correct class of fire extinguisher is used.
- Evacuate the building.
- Follow emergency signage / emergency ***evacuation plan.***
- Walk briskly but calmly, do not run.
- Feel doors for heat before opening them to be sure there is no fire danger on the other side.
- Keep the fire contained by closing windows if it is safe to do so.
- Try to rescue others only if it is safe to do so.
- Do not pick up objects that have fallen into the fire.
- If there is smoke in the air, try to stay low to the ground.
- Get to a place of safety (***assembly point***) and call the fire department.

evacuation plan: *document or diagram or sign showing the safest emergency exit routes from a building*

assembly point: *a location specified as the place for a group of people to gather in an emergency*

Activity 2.1

1.	What do you understand by a fire?	(3)
2.	List five causes of a fire (sources of heat).	(5)
3.	What is the function of a fire extinguisher?	(2)
4.	List the five classes of fire and give one type of fuel associated with each class.	(5)
5.	List five types of fire extinguishers.	(5)
6.	State five safety precautions to be observed in the event of a fire.	(5)
		TOTAL: [25]

Summary of Module 2

We have covered the following in this module. See if you have mastered each of these sections.

Unit 2.1 Fire and firefighting

- A fire is a process that occurs when a combustible material combines chemically with oxygen in the air and extreme heat, and gives off bright light, heat and smoke.
- The fire triangle shows the ingredients needed to start and sustain a fire:
  - Heat.
  - Fuel.
  - Oxygen.
- The type of fuel that contributes to the fire determines the class of fire and this also determines the type of fire extinguisher that can be used.
- The function of a fire extinguisher is to remove at least one of the elements of the fire triangle in order to put out the fire.
- In order to use a fire extinguisher correctly, remember the PASS mnemonic.
- Fire is very dangerous and it is important to follow safety precautions in the event of a fire.

Summative assessment for Module 2

1. List the three elements needed to start a fire. (3)
2. Draw up a table to show the different classes of fire, one type of fuel for each class and one type of fire extinguisher used for each class. (15)
3. State the four simple steps to be followed when using a fire extinguisher. (4)
4. List four dangers of a fire and give one detrimental effect of each danger. (8)

TOTAL: [30]

Module

3 Hand and power tools

Overview of Module 3

Tools are objects that are used to extend the ability of individuals by making work easy, or that are simply used to carry out a particular function. Hand tools depend on manual labour whereas power tools require an additional power source.

In this module we are going to identify various hand and power tools and learn about their care and maintenance.

When you have completed this module, you should be able to:

Unit 3.1: Hand tools

- Identify and explain the purpose/use of the following hand tools used by electricians:
  - Flat and Phillips screwdriver, long-nose pliers, combination pliers, diagonal pliers (side cutters), crimping tools, hacksaw, cable knife, spring bender, hickey, draw tape.
- State the care and maintenance of hand tools.

Unit 3.2: Power tools

- State the care and maintenance of power tools:
  - Fixed, portable and cordless.
- State the safety precautions to be observed when working with power tools.

Figure 3.1: Using the correct tool for the correct job

Starter activity

Discuss the following in class:

- A conduit pipe is laid in a concrete floor, linking the distribution board located in the passage and a socket outlet located in the garage. How do you think that the conductors will be pulled through from the distribution board to the socket outlet?
- Many applications still require the use of metal conduit pipes. Have you ever thought of how these pipes are bent without the walls of the pipe collapsing?
- A Phillips screwdriver. What an unusual name. Do you know what this is?

Unit 3.1: Hand tools

Definition of tool

A tool is a device, especially one held in the hand, used to carry out a particular function.

3.1.1 Basic hand tools

In Table 3.1 we look at the basic hand tools; their purpose and how to use and care for them.

Table 3.1: Basic hand tools

Hand tool	Picture	Purpose, use and care
Flat screwdriver		Screwdrivers are used to turn screws. Flat screwdrivers are used for screws with a slotted head (flat head). Phillips screwdrivers are used for screws with a Phillips head (star shape). Important: • Always use the correct size and type of screwdriver for a particular application (see Figure 3.2). • Ensure that the workpiece is carefully secured. • Ensure that the handle of the screwdriver is present and secure. • Screwdrivers must not be used as chisels, levers or scrapers. • Always keep handles clean and dry. • Screwdrivers must be correctly sharpened.
Phillips screwdriver		
Long-nose pliers		Long-nose pliers are used to twist and bend wires. They are also used to grip items in small places and in places that are hard to reach. Important: • Be careful not to apply excessive pressure in twisting thick wires. • The pivot point must be oiled regularly.

Hand tool	Picture	Purpose, use and care
Combination pliers		Combination pliers are often simply called pliers and they are very versatile. They are the most popular type of pliers. They can grip flat and round objects and can also be used to cut and twist wire. Important: • The pivot point must be oiled regularly.
Diagonal pliers (side cutters)		Diagonal pliers are used to cut wire. Important: • The pivot point must be oiled regularly.
Crimping tool		Crimping tools are used to crimp ***ferrules*** and ***lugs*** onto conductors. Some types have wire-cutting and insulation-stripping features. Important: • Be careful, as the tool can be damaged when trying to cut large conductors. • The pivot point must be oiled regularly.
Hacksaw		A hacksaw is a versatile saw used for cutting metals, plastic and wood. It has a fine-toothed blade fitted under tension into a frame. Important: • Ensure that the blade is properly tightened. • The teeth must always face forward.
Cable knife		A cable knife is used to remove the outer and inner sheaths of a cable. It is also used to remove insulation from around conductors. Important: • Ensure that you work away from your body, because this knife can cause serious injuries.
Spring bender		A spring bender is used to bend PVC conduit pipes (see Figure 3.3). The spring is inserted into the pipe and then bent by hand over your knee. The purpose of the spring bender is to prevent the walls of the pipe from collapsing (i.e. to prevent the pipe from kinking).
Hickey bender		A hickey bender is used to bend metal conduit pipes (see Figure 3.4). The purpose of the hickey bender is to prevent the walls of the pipe from collapsing (i.e. to prevent the metal pipe from kinking).

Hand tool	Picture	Purpose, use and care
Draw tape		Draw tapes are used to pull (draw) conductors through conduit pipes (see Figure 3.5). They are commonly made from steel or nylon. Important: • The conductors must be securely attached to the draw tape in order to prevent them from coming loose (see Figure 3.6). • The conductors must be staggered in order to prevent bulging.

ferrule: *a copper or aluminium tube used to join conductors*

lug: *used to terminate a conductor onto a stud or bolt*

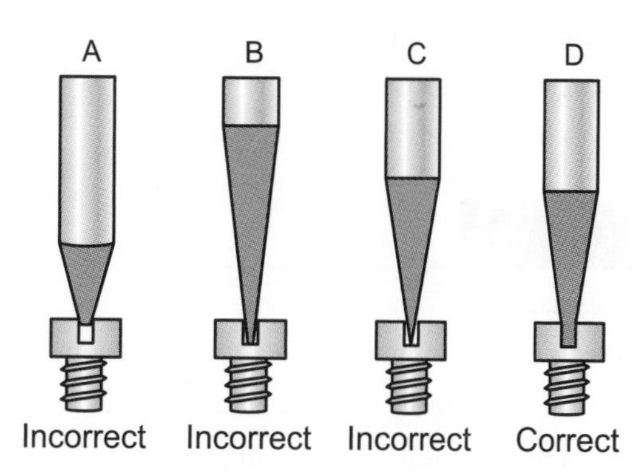

Figure 3.2: Correct use of a screwdriver

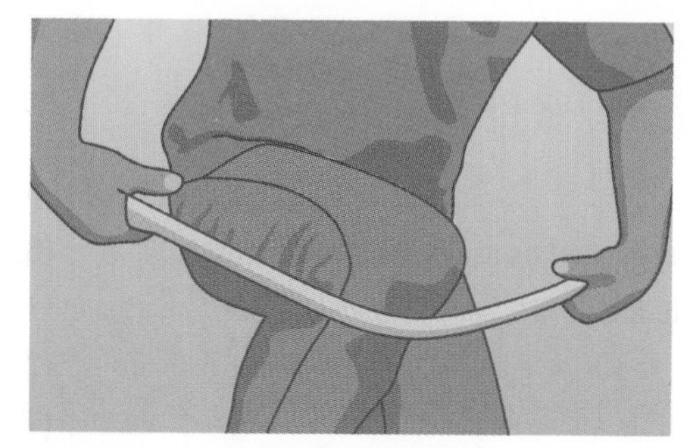

Figure 3.3: Bending PVC conduit with a spring bender

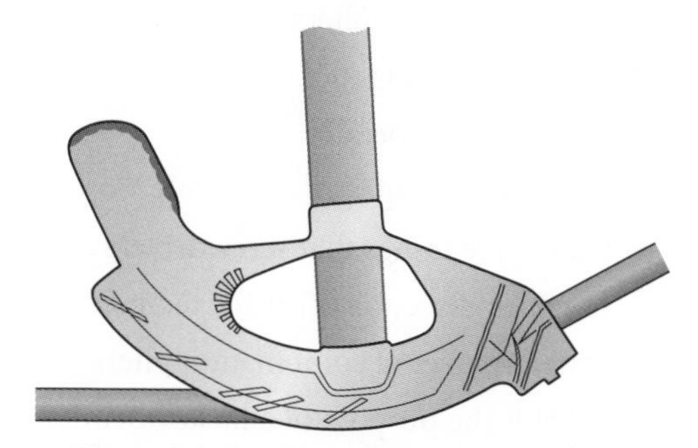

Figure 3.4: Bending a metal conduit pipe with a hickey bender

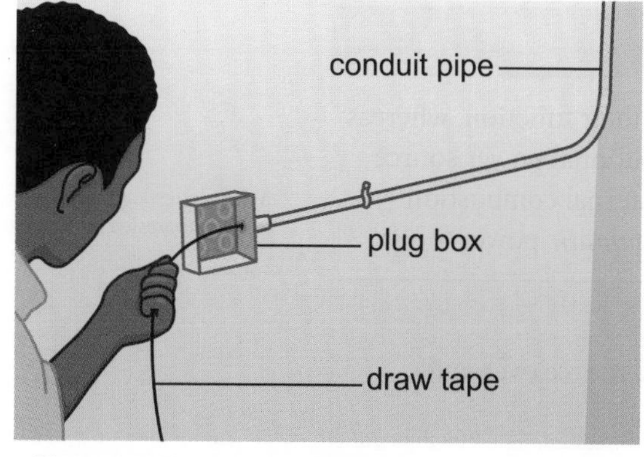

Figure 3.5: Drawing conductors through conduit pipe with a draw tape

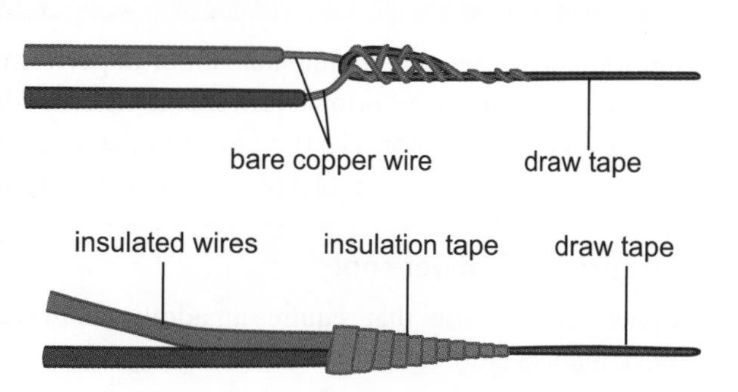

Figure 3.6: Conductors attached to a draw tape

3.1.2 General care and maintenance of hand tools

Care should be taken with hand tools:

- Always use the correct tool for the job.
- Never carry sharp tools in your pocket.
- Always replace or repair damaged tools.
- Keep tools clean and well-oiled to prevent rusting.
- Tools must be well lubricated so that they operate effectively.
- Never stack files on top of one another.
- Avoid using chisels with ***burrs***.
- Do not use a file with a missing handle.
- Never use a hammer with a loose head.
- Always return tools to their correct places after use.

burrs: *raised edges or small pieces of unwanted metal on a chisel*

Activity 3.1

1. What are tools used for? (3)
2. State five aspects concerning the care and maintenance of hand tools. (5)
3. List any five basic hand tools used by an electrician. (5)
4. State the function of the following hand tools:
   - 4.1 Long-nose pliers.
   - 4.2 Diagonal pliers.
   - 4.3 Crimping tool.
   - 4.4 Spring bender.
   - 4.5 Draw tape. $(5 \times 1 = 5)$
5. State three things that screwdrivers are used that is regarded as abuse of hand tools. (3)
6. In which direction must the teeth of a hacksaw blade face? (1)
7. State two uses of combination pliers. (2)
8. What is the purpose of a hickey bender? (1)

TOTAL: [25]

Unit 3.2: Power tools

Hand tools are dependent on manual labour to perform their function, whereas power tools require an additional power source. This additional power source could be an electric motor (electric power tools) or an internal combustion engine (combustion power tools) or compressed air (***pneumatic*** power tools).

pneumatic: *operated by gas or compressed air*

Definition of power tool

A power tool is a tool that requires an additional power source over and above manual labour.

Power tools are widely used in industry and in the home.

They can be fixed (stationary) or portable (handheld):

- **Fixed power tools:** They are mounted on a stand or bolted to the floor. They cannot be easily moved, for example a lathe, drill press, bench grinder or table saw.
- **Portable power tools:** They are handheld and can be moved around easily. Portable power tools can be either corded or cordless. Examples include drills, jigsaws and belt sanders.

It is very important to care for and maintain all power tools because this will ensure:

- Longer lifespan.
- Safety.
- Better quality of operation.

In this unit we will look at the following in more detail:

- Pneumatic tools.
- Fixed electric power tools.
- Portable electric power tools.

3.2.1 Pneumatic tools

Definition of a pneumatic tool

A pneumatic tool is a power tool that is powered by compressed air supplied by an air compressor. These tools are also called air tools.

Pneumatic tools can be either fixed or portable.

The following are some types of pneumatic tools that are available:

- Grinders.
- Drills.
- Wrenches.
- Sanders and buffers.
- Jackhammers.
- Paint sprayers.
- Nail guns.

Figure 3.7: Air compressor

Figure 3.8: Using a jackhammer

Care and maintenance of pneumatic tools

The following should be done to care for and maintain all types of pneumatic tools (fixed and portable):

- Check for loose screws.
- Clean the tools after use.
- Clean the feed system.
- Regularly lubricate all moving parts.
- Drain the receiver tanks.
- Check for leaks along the airline.
- Always ensure correct air pressure.
- Check and replace any damaged or worn-out seals, gaskets, O-rings and couplers.

Safety precautions concerning pneumatic tools

The following safety precautions should always be observed when working with pneumatic tools:

- Always turn off the air pressure to the hose supplying the tool when it is not in use, or when changing or inspecting or repairing the tool.
- Never carry around a power tool by its supply hose.
- Avoid creating trip hazards by laying the supply hose across walkways.
- Do not use compressed air to blow away debris. Also, do not clean clothes or dust off yourself by using compressed air.
- Do not operate power tools at a pressure above the manufacturer's rating.

3.2.2 Electric tools

Definition of an electric power tool

An electric power tool is a power tool that is powered by an electric motor that is supplied by either a battery (cordless power tool) or an electricity socket.

Electric power tools can be either portable or fixed.

Figure 3.9: Electric power tools can be fixed or portable

Examples of electric power tools include:

- Grinders.
- Sanders.
- Saws.
- Drills.
- Screwdrivers.
- Wrenches.
- Lathes.
- Joiners.
- Jointers.

Fixed electric power tools

When working with fixed power tools such as a drill press or a bench grinder, special safety precautions must be observed.

Drill press

A drill press is a machine used to make or enlarge round holes. It may be mounted on a stand or bolted to the floor.

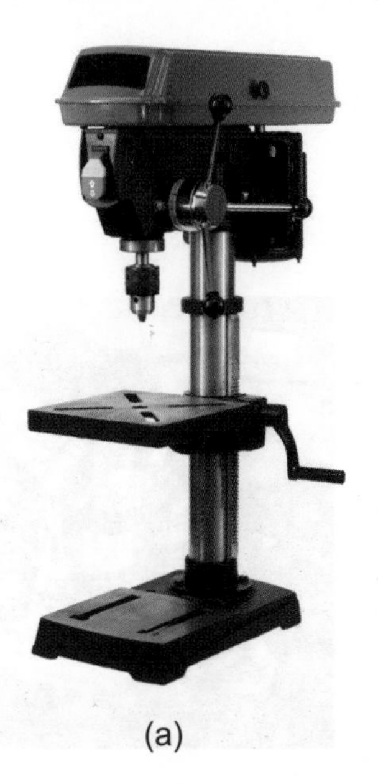

(a)

(b)

Figure 3.10: (a) A drill press and (b) maintaining a drill press

Safety precautions concerning drill presses

The following safety precautions should always be observed when working with a drill press:

- Clear the area around the drill press.
- Dress appropriately. Do not wear loose clothing and tie up long hair.
- Use the correct drill bit and ensure that it is secure.
- Secure the workpiece.
- Use the drill press at the correct speed.
- Do not clean away metal pieces with your fingers.
- Do not leave the machine running while it is unattended.

- Never use your hands to stop the chuck from spinning after the machine has been switched off.

Care and maintenance of drill presses

Look after your drill press by doing the following:

- Always clean the drill press after use.
- Check that all parts are present and secure.
- Lubricate all moving parts regularly using the correct lubricant.
- Check the condition and tension of the drive belt.
- Check the condition of the supply cable.
- Check that the switch functions correctly.
- Check the condition of the ***drill quill*** and check for any sideway play.

drill quill: *the hollow shaft surrounding the spindle to which the chuck is mounted*

chuck: *a specialised clamp used to hold the rotating drill bit in position*

grinding wheel: *a wheel or disk made of **abrasive** material used in grinding machines for cutting or smoothing hard materials*

abrasive: *rough or coarse*

gouges: *chisels with a concave blade used in carpentry*

Bench grinder

A bench grinder is a machine with two ***grinding wheels***.

Grinding wheels are used for:

- Sharpening cutting tools such as tool bits, drill bits, chisels and ***gouges***.
- Shaping metal pieces.
- Cleaning.
- Buffing and polishing metal pieces.

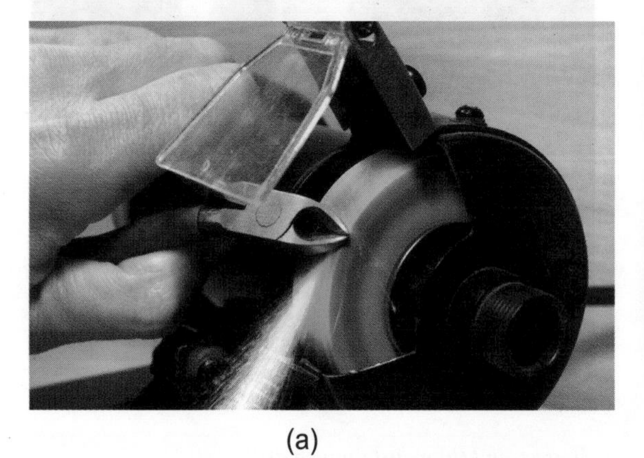

(a)

(b)

Figure 3.11: (a) A grinding wheel and (b) using a grinding wheel

Safety precautions concerning bench grinders

The following safety precautions must be observed when working with grinding wheels:

- Choose the correct type of wheel for the job.
- Look for cracks.
- Make sure that the manufacturer's recommended wheel speed is not exceeded.
- Do not alter the hole size in the wheel or force the wheel onto the spindle.
- Use eye protection or adjust the eye shield on the grinder.

- Check that the tool rest is not more than 3 mm from the wheel and is square to it.
- Before you start grinding, step aside and let the wheel run freely.
- Place the workpiece against the face of the wheel and not against its side.
- Do not force the workpiece onto the wheel. It may cause the wheel to stall or slow down.
- Do not grind materials such as lead, aluminium and brass, because clogging of the wheel causes poor cutting and overheating.

The following factors could cause a grinding wheel to fracture:

- Working at speeds higher than those recommended by the manufacturer.
- Excessive heating caused by the grinding process.
- Forcing the workpiece against the wheel.
- Tension on the wheel caused by incorrect assembly.
- Imbalance caused by moisture.

Care and maintenance of a bench grinder

Care for and maintain your bench grinder as follows:

- Always clean the bench grinder after use.
- Check that all parts are present and secure, especially the tool rest.
- Lubricate all moving parts regularly using the correct lubricant.
- Check the condition of the supply cable.
- Check that the switch functions correctly.
- Dress the grinding wheel regularly.
- Know when to replace the wheel.

Portable electric power tools

Portable power tools are handheld and can be easily moved around. They can be either corded (run off a socket outlet) or cordless (run off batteries).

Figure 3.12: Portable electric power tools

When working with portable power tools, there are some safety and maintenance considerations.

Care and maintenance of portable electric power tools

To care for and maintain portable electric power tools, do the following:

- Always clean the tools before storing them away.
- Store the tools in a dry, clean, safe and well-ventilated area.
- Use compressed air to clean out tool vents.
- Regularly lubricate moving parts.
- Tighten all parts that may have come loose during operation.
- Check for damaged supply cables (cords).
- Always use the correct blade or bit for the job.

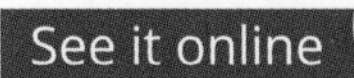

Caring for tools
Learn more about maintaining both hand and power tools in this video – How to Maintain Your Tools by eReplacementParts.com | https://youtu.be/DuU2mnJcxPM

Care and maintenance of batteries for cordless tools

Cordless portable tools run off batteries which need to be used with care and maintained properly:

- Always ensure that the battery, battery charger and the power tool are all compatible.
- Always recharge the battery when you notice poor performance of the tools.
- Lithium-ion batteries should not be discharged completely before recharging.
- Once nickel-based batteries get hot, stop the machine and allow the battery to cool.
- If lithium-ion batteries get hot, this means that the battery is damaged and must be replaced.
- Always unplug the charger between uses in order to prevent any accidental short circuits.
- Store the battery charger away after use.
- Avoid overcharging nickel-based batteries.
- Batteries are best charged in temperatures between 4 °C and 29 °C.

Safety precautions concerning portable electric power tools

The following are special safety practices for portable electric power tools:

- Portable power tools must be inspected regularly for visible defects.
- Check for broken plug tops.
- Check for damaged or missing insulation.
- Check if the switch is functioning properly.
- Check for broken or missing covers.
- Use the correct cutting discs and drill bits for the job.
- Check that the cutting discs and drill bits are properly tightened.
- Always ensure that the workpiece is properly secured.
- Avoid working in wet areas.
- Dress appropriately. Do not wear loose clothing and tie up long hair.

Figure 3.13: Using a portable electric power tool

Activity 3.2

1. State the additional power source needed to operate a pneumatic tool. (1)
2. State three reasons why the care and maintenance of power tools is important. (3)
3. State five aspects concerning the care and maintenance of pneumatic tools. (5)
4. State two sources of energy that can be used to supply electric power tools. (2)
5. State three aspects concerning the care and maintenance of electric power tools. (3)
6. State three aspects concerning the care and maintenance of the batteries used in cordless power tools. (3)
7. State three safety precautions to be observed with portable power tools. (3)

TOTAL: [20]

Summary of Module 3

We have covered the following in this module. See if you have mastered each of these sections.

Unit 3.1 Hand tools

- A tool is a device, especially one held in the hand, used to carry out a particular function.
- Screwdrivers must not be used as chisels, levers or scrapers.
- Long-nose pliers are used to twist and bend wires and also to grip items in small places and places that are hard to reach.
- Combination pliers are very versatile and the most popular type of pliers.
- Diagonal pliers are used to cut wire.
- Crimping tools are used to crimp lugs and ferrules onto conductors.
- A hacksaw is a very versatile saw used for cutting metals, plastic and wood.
- A cable knife is used to remove insulation from around conductors.
- A spring bender is used to bend PVC conduit pipes.
- A hickey bender is used to bend metal conduit pipes.
- A draw tape is used to pull (draw) conductors through conduit pipes.

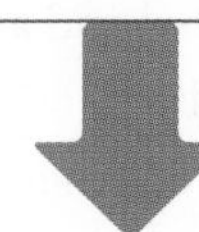

Unit 3.2 Power tools

- Power tools require an additional power source to perform their function.
- Power tools can be either:
  - Fixed (stationary).
  - Portable (corded or cordless).
- It is important to care for and maintain all power tools because it ensures:
  - A longer lifespan.
  - Safety.
  - Better quality of operation.
- Pneumatic tools need compressed air in order to operate.
- Electric power tools can be supplied either off a socket outlet or by a battery (cordless power tool).
- A drill press is a machine used to make or enlarge round holes. It may be mounted on a stand or bolted to the floor.
- A bench grinder is a machine used to drive abrasive grinding wheels to sharpen cutting tools and to shape, clean, buff and polish.

Summative assessment for Module 3

1. Name two types of screwdrivers with which you are familiar. (2)

2. State the function of the following hand tools:

- **2.1** Hacksaw.
- **2.2** Cable knife.
- **2.3** Screwdriver. ($3 \times 1 = 3$)

3. Name two types of draw tape. (2)

4. State one safety precaution to be observed when working with a cable knife. (1)

5. Explain how a spring bender is used to bend PVC conduit pipes. (2)

6. What is the purpose of a hickey bender? (1)

7. What is the difference between a hand tool and a power tool? (3)

8. List three types of pneumatic power tools. (3)

9. State five safety precautions to be observed when working with grinding wheels. (5)

10. State three factors that could cause a grinding wheel to fracture. (3)

TOTAL: [25]

Direct current (DC) circuit theory

Module

4

direct current (DC): *electric current that flows in one direction only*

dissipate: *cause energy to be lost through its conversion into heat*

Overview of Module 4

Energy cannot be created or destroyed, but it can be converted from one form into another. ***Direct current*** (DC) electrical energy is stored in batteries in the form of chemical energy and converted into electrical energy when needed.

In this module we are going to learn how to solve electric circuits supplied from a DC source.

When you have completed this module, you should be able to:

Editorial Credit: Wikimedia Commons

Figure 4.1: Georg Simon Ohm was a German physicist and mathematician who developed laws for electricity

Unit 4.1: Basic electricity, Ohm's law and Joule's law

- State what is meant by:
  - Current.
  - Potential difference (voltage).
  - Resistance.
- State Ohm's law.
- State Joule's law.
- Use Joule's law to determine the heat energy ***dissipated*** in electrical circuits.
- Calculate the cost of electrical energy (kW × hours × tariff).

Unit 4.2: Methods of connecting resistors in a circuit

- Use Ohm's law to determine current, voltage, resistance, volt drop and power in a circuit having resistance connected in series, parallel and series-parallel (maximum four resistors).

Unit 4.3: Factors influencing the resistance of a conductor

- State the factors that affect the resistance of a conductor.
- State what is meant by resistivity.
- Calculate the resistance of a conductor at constant temperature.
- Define temperature coefficient of resistance.
- State how temperature affects the resistance of pure metals, alloys, carbon, electrolytes and insulators.
- Explain the difference between positive and negative temperature coefficients.
- Calculate the resistance of a conductor at any temperature with the initial resistance given at zero degrees Celsius.

Unit 4.4: Cells and batteries

- State the function of a cell or battery.
- Differentiate between primary and secondary cells.
- Explain with the aid of a circuit the difference between emf and potential difference.

- Calculate the total emf and internal resistance of cells connected in series and parallel.
- Calculate the total current in a circuit using the total emf.

Starter activity

Discuss the following in class:

- Electricity is our most useful form of energy. Where do you think electricity comes from?
- Friction ***opposes*** motion. Without friction we would be slipping and sliding every time we try to move. Resistance opposes current flow. Do you think that resistance serves any useful purpose?
- From your previous knowledge of unit conversion, can you convert 120 mm^2 to m^2?

oppose: *work against*

Unit 4.1: Basic electricity, Ohm's law and Joule's law

Everything that we find around us is called matter. Matter exists in one of three forms: solid, liquid and gas.

Matter is made up of tiny particles called molecules, which in turn are made up of even smaller particles called ***atoms***.

An atom in its simplest form has a ***nucleus*** at its centre surrounded by shells or ***orbitals*** (see Figure 4.2). The nucleus contains ***protons*** (+ charges) and ***neutrons*** (no electrical charge). The nucleus is therefore positively charged.

Electrons (– charges) are found in the surrounding orbitals. The electrons located in the outermost orbital are called ***valence electrons***. Because there are only very small forces of attraction between valence electrons and the positively charged nucleus, valence electrons in certain materials can easily detach themselves from the parent atom and become charge carriers.

atom: *the smallest particle of an element*
nucleus: *the centre of an atom that is made up of protons and neutrons*
orbital: *the path followed by an electron around the nucleus of an atom*
proton: *positive-charge carrier*
neutron: *particle with no electrical charge*
electron: *negative-charge carrier*
valence electron: *electron in the outermost orbital of an atom*

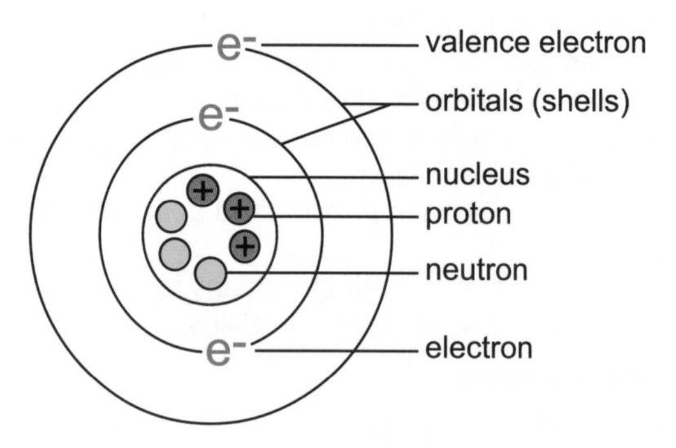

Figure 4.2: A simple atom

4.1.1 Current

elementary charge: *charge carried by a single electron*

electricity (current flow): *flow of charge (electrons) in a specific direction*

conventional current flow: *flow of current from the positive terminal of a battery to the negative terminal of the battery*

electron flow: *the flow of current from the negative terminal of a battery to the positive terminal of the battery*

circuit: *a movement that starts and finishes at the same point*

closed electric circuit: *a complete electrical connection around which current flows*

terminal voltage: *potential difference between the terminals of a cell when current flows*

Definition of current

The movement or flow of negative-charge carriers (electrons) in a specific direction is called current.

Current is represented by the symbol I and is measured in amperes (A).

Definition of ampere

The ampere is a unit of electric current equal to a flow of one coulomb (C) per second, where the fixed numerical value of the ***elementary charge*** e is taken to be $1{,}602176634 \times 10^{-19}$ when given in coulomb.

[Note: This is the new internationally accepted definition as of 20/05/2019.]

The movement or flow of electrons in a specific direction is what we call ***electricity***.

Direction of current flow

In the old days, it was believed that electrons flow from the positive terminal of a battery to the negative terminal. This is known as the ***conventional flow of current***. Later, it was discovered that electrons actually flow from the negative terminal to the positive terminal of a battery. This is known as ***electron flow***.

Electricity is needed by domestic and industrial consumers for the following effects that current flow produces:

- Lighting.
- Heating.
- Chemical effects.
- Magnetic effects.

4.1.2 Potential difference

The flow of current through a ***circuit*** depends on the application of a potential difference across any two points in the electric circuit.

Definition of potential difference

The potential difference between two points in a circuit is the work done when 1 coulomb of charge is moved from one point to the other.

Simply put, potential difference is an electrical pressure that produces current flow in a ***closed electric circuit***. It is also known as ***terminal voltage***.

Potential difference is represented by the symbol V or PD and is measured in joules per coulomb or volts.

4.1.3 Electromotive force

Electromotive force is an electrical potential produced by any source of electrical energy. Its function is to initiate and maintain a potential difference. Electromotive force (emf) is represented by the symbol E and is also measured in volts (V).

> **Definition of electromotive force (emf)**
>
> Electromotive force is the voltage measured across the ends of an energy source of an ***open circuit***. (Remember that *no* current is flowing in an open circuit.)

Sources of electromotive force

The following are sources of electromotive force or sources of electrical energy:

- Cells or batteries.
- ***Generators***.
- ***Solar energy***.
- Heat.
- ***Friction***.

Important

Electromotive force versus potential difference

Did you notice that potential difference and electromotive force are both measured in volts? Over the years people have started to refer to both potential difference and electromotive force as **voltage** (which also means electrical potential). So, let us talk about the differences between the two in order to avoid confusion.

Electromotive force (emf) is the voltage (electrical potential) measured across the terminals of an electrical energy source of an *open circuit*. This means that *no* current is flowing through the circuit.

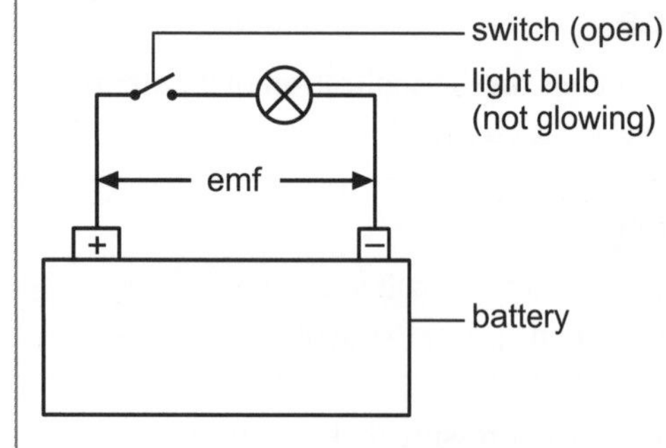

- The switch is open.
- Current does not flow, so the light bulb does not glow.
- The emf is measured across the energy source (the battery in this case).

Figure 4.3: Emf in an electric circuit

Potential difference (PD) is the voltage (electrical potential) measured across the terminals of an electrical energy source of a *closed circuit*. This means that there *is* current flowing through the circuit.

→

open circuit: *an incomplete electrical connection through which current cannot flow*

generator: *a machine that converts one form of energy into another, especially mechanical energy into electrical energy*

solar energy: *radiant energy emitted by the sun*

radiant: *sending out light; shining or glowing brightly*

friction: *the resistance that one surface experiences when moving over another*

misnomer: *a word or concept suggesting a meaning that is known to be wrong*

Interesting

Electromotive 'force' is a ***misnomer***. It is not a force measured in newtons, but an electrical potential.

See it online

Emf vs PD
Learn more in this video – Electromotive Force and Potential Difference by Chriz Gozzard | https://youtu.be/WsT7LfuH7Tg

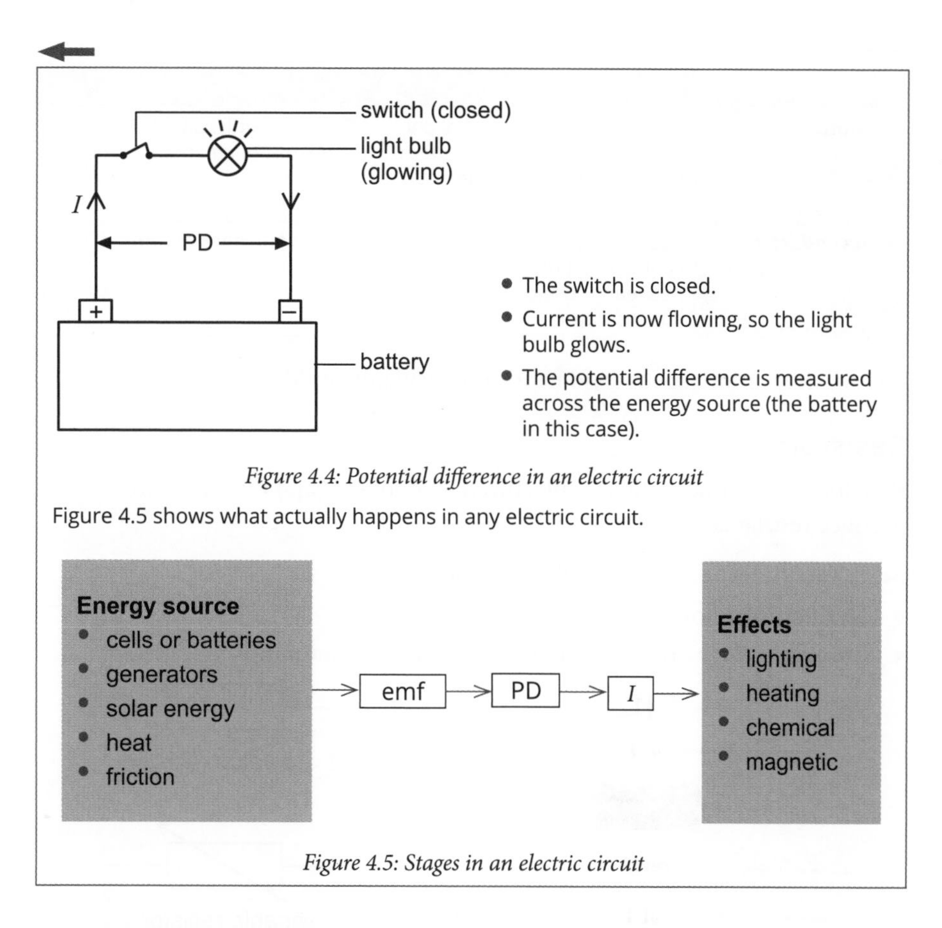

Figure 4.4: Potential difference in an electric circuit

Figure 4.5 shows what actually happens in any electric circuit.

Figure 4.5: Stages in an electric circuit

4.1.4 Resistance

All materials have resistance. Resistance opposes current flow.

Definition of resistance

Resistance is the opposition that a substance offers to the flow of electric current. In this process heat is produced.

Resistance is represented by the symbol R and is measured in ohms (Ω).

Classification of materials

Materials used in the electrical industry are classified as shown in Table 4.1:

Table 4.1: Classification of materials

Type of material	Description	Examples
Conductors	Substances that allow current to flow through them. These substances may be good or poor conductors: • Good conductors have very low resistance values. • Poor conductors have high resistance values.	**Good conductors** Pure metals such as gold, silver, copper and aluminium **Poor conductors** Steel, lead and ***tungsten***

Note

Tungsten is a very poor conductor of electricity. It is highly resistent to the flow of current. It is used to manufacture the ***filaments*** of ***incandescent*** light bulbs.

filament: *a conducting wire with a high melting point, forming part of an electric bulb that is made incandescent by passing an electric current through it*

conductor: *any substance that allows current to flow through it*

tungsten: *a dense, greyish white metal with a high melting point; also called wolfram*

Type of material	Description	Examples
Insulators	Substances that do not allow current to pass through them. Insulators have very high resistance.	Glass, ceramic, paper, ***PVC***, asbestos, ***mica*** and porcelain
Semiconductors	Substances that have conducting properties that lie between those of conductors and insulators.	Silicon and germanium

You will learn more about conductors and insulators in Module 5.

Resistors

Resistors are commercially manufactured components and their function is to produce resistance.

Resistance is needed in electrical circuits to:

- Limit current flow.
- Produce ***voltage drops*** (which will be discussed later in this module).

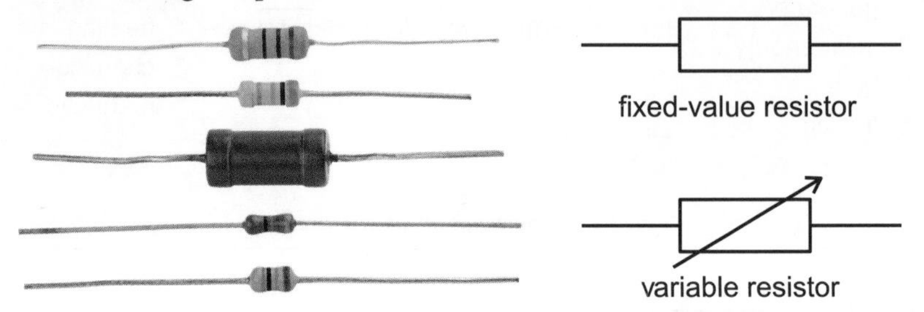

Figure 4.6: Resistors and their ***IEC*** *symbols*

A circuit containing only resistors is known as a ***resistive circuit***.

4.1.5 Ohm's law

Resistance, current and potential difference in any closed circuit have a specific relationship between them. This relationship is given by Ohm's law, a law that was discovered by and named after Georg Simon Ohm, a German physicist and mathematician.

Ohm's law

Ohm's law states that:

The current flowing in any closed circuit is ***directly proportional*** *to the voltage producing it and* ***inversely proportional*** *to the resistance of the circuit, provided the temperature remains constant.*

Ohm's law is expressed as follows:

$$I = \frac{V}{R}$$

insulator: *a substance that does not allow current to flow through it easily*

PVC: *polyvinyl chloride*

mica: *a silicate mineral found in granite and other rocks that is used as a thermal or electrical insulator*

semiconductor: *a solid substance that has a conductivity between that of an insulator and that of a conductor*

resistor: *an electrical component that limits or regulates the flow of electric current in an electric circuit*

voltage drop: *the decrease of electrical potential along the path of a current flowing in an electric circuit*

IEC: *International Electrotechnical Commission, the body responsible for recommending internationally accepted symbols and units*

resistive circuit: *any circuit containing resistance only*

directly proportional: *the bigger one value, the bigger another value; for example, the bigger the voltage, the bigger the current (Ohm's law)*

inversely proportional: *the bigger one value, the smaller another value; for example, the bigger the resistance, the smaller the current (Ohm's law)*

See it online

Resistors
Learn more about resistors by watching this video – Electronics – Resistors by ScienceOnline | https://youtu.be/HrZZMhWZiFk

The following website is a great resource: resistorguide.com

where:

- I = current in amperes (A).
- R = resistance in ohms (Ω).
- V = potential difference in volts (V).

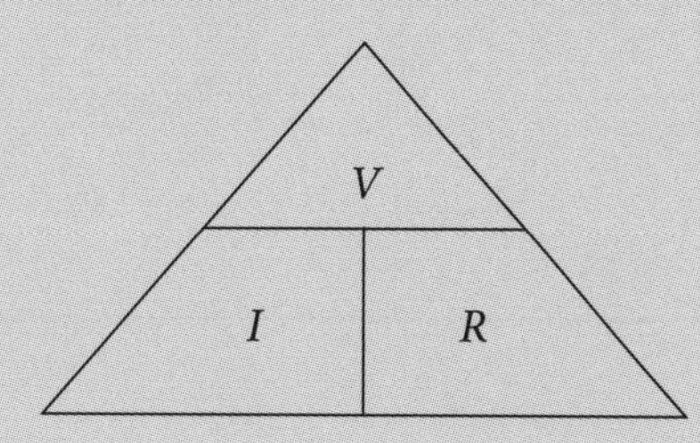

From the triangle, we get:

- $V = IR$
- $I = \frac{V}{R}$
- $R = \frac{V}{I}$

Figure 4.7: Triangle for Ohm's law

Exam tip

When giving a solution to any question that needs a calculation, you must show the following:

1. The formula used.
2. Substitution into the formula.
3. The unit of measurement.
4. Correct answer to three decimal places.

Example 4.1

A 10 Ω resistor is connected across a 12 V supply. Calculate the current drawn from the supply.

Solution

Given:

$V = 12$ V $R = 10$ Ω

$$I = \frac{V}{R} = \frac{12}{10} = 1{,}2 \text{ A}$$

Example 4.2

An ***electrical load*** draws 5,5 A of current from a 200 V supply. Determine the resistance of the load.

electrical load: *anything that requires current to operate*

Solution

Given: $V = 200$ V $I = 5{,}5$ A

$$R = \frac{V}{I} = \frac{200}{5{,}5} = 36{,}364 \ \Omega$$

Example 4.3

A light bulb with a resistance of 12,5 Ω draws 4,8 A of current from the supply. Calculate the potential difference of the supply.

Solution

Given: $R = 12{,}5\ \Omega$ $\quad\quad I = 4{,}8\ \text{A}$

$V = IR$

$= (4{,}8)(12{,}5)$

$= 60\ \text{V}$

Activity 4.1

1. State the three forms in which matter can exist. (3)
2. What are valence electrons? (1)
3. Explain what is meant by current flow. (2)
4. State the four effects of an electric current. (4)
5. State the difference between emf and potential difference. (4)
6. State three sources of emf. (3)
7. What do you understand by resistance? (3)
8. State two functions of resistors in electrical circuits. (2)
9. Draw the IEC symbol for the following:
   - 9.1 Fixed-value resistor. (1)
   - 9.2 Variable resistor. (2)
10. Explain the following terms:
    - 10.1 Conductors. (2)
    - 10.2 Insulators. (2)
11. State Ohm's law. (4)
12. A piece of nichrome wire that is used as a heater element has a resistance of 25 Ω. Calculate the current that this heater element will draw from a 240 V supply. (2)
13. A geyser element draws 12 A of current from a 230 V supply. Calculate the resistance of the element. (2)
14. A light bulb with a resistance of 24 Ω draws a current of 5 A from the supply. Calculate the potential difference of the supply. (2)
15. A variable resistor is connected to a 200 V supply. Calculate:
    - 15.1 The current drawn from the supply if the resistor is set at 50 Ω. (2)
    - 15.2 The current drawn from the supply if the resistor is set at 100 Ω. (2)
    - 15.3 The current drawn from the supply if the resistor is set at 50 Ω, but the supply voltage is increased to 400 V. (2)

TOTAL: [45]

4.1.6 Power in a resistive circuit

Definition of power

Power is the rate at which work is done or the rate at which energy is consumed.

Power is represented by the symbol P and is measured in watts (W).

Formulae for calculating power

Power is calculated using the following formulae:

- $P = VI$
- $P = (IR)I$ [Substituting $V = IR$]
  $= I^2R$
- $P = V\left(\frac{V}{R}\right)$ $\left[\text{Substituting } I = \frac{V}{R}\right]$
  $= \frac{V^2}{R}$

where:

- P = power in watts (W).
- V = potential difference in volts (V).
- I = current in amperes (A).
- R = resistance in ohms (Ω).

Example 4.4

A light bulb draws 3 A of current from a 12 V supply.

Calculate:

1. The resistance of the bulb.
2. The ***power rating*** of the bulb.

power rating (bulb): *the amount of electrical energy that a bulb will convert into light and heat energy in 1 second*

Solution

Given: $I = 3$ A $V = 12$ V

1. $R = \frac{V}{I}$
   $= \frac{12}{3}$
   $= 4\ \Omega$

2. $P = VI$ or $P = I^2R$ or $P = \frac{V^2}{R}$

   $P = VI = (12)(3) = 36$ W

   or $P = I^2R = (3)^2(4) = 36$ W

   or $P = \frac{V^2}{R} = \frac{(12)^2}{4} = 36$ W

Example 4.5

An electrical appliance rated at 1 000 W has a supply voltage of 220 V. Calculate:

1. The current drawn by the appliance.
2. The resistance of the appliance.

Solution

Given: $P = 1\ 000$ W $V = 220$ V

1. $I = \frac{P}{V}$

$= \frac{1\ 000}{220}$

$= 4{,}545$ A

2. $R = \frac{V}{I}$

$= \frac{220}{4{,}545}$

$= 48{,}405\ \Omega$

or $P = I^2R$

$R = \frac{P}{I^2}$

$= \frac{1\ 000}{(4{,}545)^2}$

$= 48{,}410\ \Omega$

or $P = \frac{V^2}{R}$

$R = \frac{V^2}{P}$

$= \frac{(220)^2}{1\ 000}$

$= 48{,}4\ \Omega$

4.1.7 Energy in an electric circuit

Definition of energy

Energy is the capacity for doing work.

Heat energy and Joule's law

We have already seen that current has a heating effect. This heat is produced when current is opposed by the resistance of the circuit.

Good conductors of electricity, such as silver, copper and aluminium, have very low resistance values and therefore cannot be used as heating elements.

Poor conductors of electricity, such as tungsten and nichrome, have high resistance values and can be used as heating elements.

Heat energy is represented by the symbol Q and is measured in joules (J).

James Prescott Joule was an English physicist who formulated a law in 1842. This law was named after him.

Important

- 1 kilojoule (kJ) = 1 000 J or 1×10^3 J
- 1 megajoule (MJ) = 1 000 000 J or 1×10^6 J
- 1 min = 60 s
- 1 h = 1 × 60
= 60 min
= 1 × 60 × 60
= 3 600 s
- To convert from joules (J) to kilojoules (kJ), divide by 1 000 or multiply by 10^{-3}.
- To convert from joules (J) to megajoules (MJ), divide by 1 000 000 or multiply by 10^{-6}.

Note

Table 4.2 in Unit 4.3 contains a method for converting between units.

Important

Note that domestic consumers are supplied with ***alternating current*** (AC). We will use this direct current (DC) section only to demonstrate and explain how consumers are billed for the energy that they consume.

alternating current (AC): *current that reverses its direction of flow many times per second*

Heat energy and Joule's law

Joule's law states that:

The heat generated in an electric circuit is proportional to the product of:

- *the square of the current* (I^2),
- *the resistance of the circuit* (R) *and*
- *the time* (t) *during which the current flows.*

Joule's law is expressed as:

$Q = I^2Rt$

where:

- Q = heat energy in joules (J).
- I = current in amperes (A).
- R = resistance in ohms (Ω).
- t = time in seconds (s).

The above formula is used to calculate heat energy.

The formula can also be written as follows:

- $Q = Pt$ [Remember, $P = I^2R$]
- $Q = VIt$ [Remember, $P = VI$]
- $Q = \frac{V^2}{R}t$ [Remember, $P = \frac{V^2}{R}$]

Energy charges

The electrical supply authorities (Eskom or municipalities) bill their domestic consumers as follows:

The cost of electricity

The cost of electricity can be calculated with the following formula:

Cost of electricity = x × kWh

where:

- x = tariff per unit of energy consumed.
- kWh = units of energy consumed.

So, what is 1 kWh?

$$\begin{aligned} 1\text{ kWh} &= 1 \text{ unit of energy} \\ &= (1\text{ kW})(1\text{ h}) \\ &= (1 \times 1\,000)(1 \times 60 \times 60) \\ &= (1\,000\text{ W})(3\,600\text{ s}) \\ &= 3\,600\,000\text{ J} \\ &= 3{,}6\text{ MJ} \end{aligned}$$

Therefore, 3,6 MJ of energy = 1 kWh.

Example 4.6

A light bulb rated at 250 W has a supply voltage of 230 V.

Calculate:

1. The current drawn by the bulb.
2. The resistance of the bulb's element.
3. The energy dissipated by the bulb in 45 minutes. Give your answer in kJ.
4. The cost to operate the bulb if the bulb works for 10 hours per night and 30 nights per month. Take the cost of energy to be 182c/kWh.

Solution

Given: $P = 250$ W $\quad V = 230$ V

1. $I = \frac{P}{V}$

$= \frac{250}{230}$

$= 1{,}087$ A

2. $R = \frac{V}{I}$

$= \frac{230}{1{,}087}$

$= 211{,}592\ \Omega$

or $P = \frac{V^2}{R}$

$R = \frac{V^2}{P}$

$= \frac{230^2}{250}$

$= 211{,}6\ \Omega$

or $R = \frac{P}{I^2}$

$= \frac{250}{1{,}087^2}$

$= 211{,}583\ \Omega$

3. $Q = Pt$

$= (250)(45 \times 60)$

$= 675\ 000$ J

$= 675$ kJ

or $Q = I^2Rt$

$= (1{,}087)^2(211{,}583)(45 \times 60)$

$= 675\ 000$ J

$= 675$ kJ

4. Total number of hours of operation $= 10 \times 30$

$= 300$ hours

kW rating of bulb $= \frac{250}{1\ 000}$

$= 0{,}25$ kW

Total energy of units of energy $= (0{,}25)(300)$

$= 75$ kWh

Cost of energy $= (75)(182)$

$= 13\ 650$c

$=$ R136,50

Example 4.7

A heating element with a resistance of 37 Ω dissipates 62,5 MJ of energy in 11 hours.

Calculate:

1. The time in seconds.
2. The current drawn from the supply.
3. The potential difference of the supply.
4. The cost of energy consumed by this element in 11 hours if energy costs 182c/kWh.

Solution

Given: $R = 37\ \Omega$ $\quad Q = 62{,}5$ MJ $\quad t = 11$ hours

1. $t = 11 \times 60 \times 60 = 39\ 600$ s
2. $Q = I^2Rt$

$$I^2Rt = Q$$
$$I^2 = \frac{Q}{Rt}$$
$$I = \sqrt{\frac{Q}{Rt}}$$
$$= \sqrt{\frac{62{,}5 \times 10^6}{(37)(39\ 600)}}$$
$$= 6{,}531 \text{ A}$$

3. $V = IR$

$$= (6{,}531)(37)$$
$$= 241{,}647 \text{ V}$$

or

$$Q = \frac{V^2}{R}t$$
$$\frac{V^2}{R}t = Q$$
$$\frac{V^2}{R} = \frac{Q}{t}$$
$$V^2 = \frac{QR}{t}$$
$$V = \sqrt{\frac{QR}{t}}$$
$$= \sqrt{\frac{(62{,}5 \times 10^6)(37)}{39\ 600}}$$
$$= 241{,}654 \text{ V}$$

4. kW rating of element $= \frac{VI}{1\ 000}$

$$= \frac{(241{,}647)(6{,}531)}{1\ 000}$$
$$= 1{,}578 \text{ kW}$$

Number of units of energy = (1,578)(11)
= 17,358 kWh

Cost of energy = (17,358)(182)
= 3 159,156c
= R31,59

Activity 4.2

1. Define power. (2)
2. Complete the table below. (4)

Quantity	Symbol	Unit of measurement
Power		
Energy		

3. State Joule's law. (4)
4. A light bulb draws 5 A of current from a 200 V supply. Calculate:
   - 4.1 The resistance of the bulb's element. (2)
   - 4.2 The power rating of the bulb. (2)
   - 4.3 The energy dissipated by the bulb in 1,5 hours. Give your answer in MJ. (3)
5. An electric iron is rated at 1,2 kW and operates at 240 V. Calculate:
   - 5.1 The current drawn from the supply. (2)
   - 5.2 The resistance of the heating element. (2)
   - 5.3 The heat energy generated by the iron in 15 minutes. (3)
6. A 240 V electrical appliance draws 12,5 A of current from the supply. Determine:
   - 6.1 The power rating of the appliance. (2)
   - 6.2 The resistance of the appliance. (2)
   - 6.3 The energy dissipated by the appliance in half an hour. (3)
7. A bakery oven dissipates 100 MJ of energy in 5 hours. If the oven operates at 240 V, calculate:
   - 7.1 The time in seconds. (2)
   - 7.2 The power rating of the element. (2)
   - 7.3 The current drawn from the supply. (2)
   - 7.4 The resistance of the element. (2)
   - 7.5 The cost to operate this oven for a month if the oven operates for 5 hours per day and 24 days per month. Take the energy cost to be 182c/kWh. (3)
8. Calculate how much it will cost to run a swimming pool pump rated at 0,75 kW if the pump runs for 3 hours per day and 30 days per month. The unit energy charge is 182 c/kWh. (3)

TOTAL: [45]

Unit 4.2: Methods of connecting resistors in a circuit

The following methods are used to connect resistors in a circuit:

- In series.
- In parallel.
- In series-parallel.

4.2.1 Resistors connected in series

Figure 4.8 shows how three resistors are connected in series and across a common voltage source.

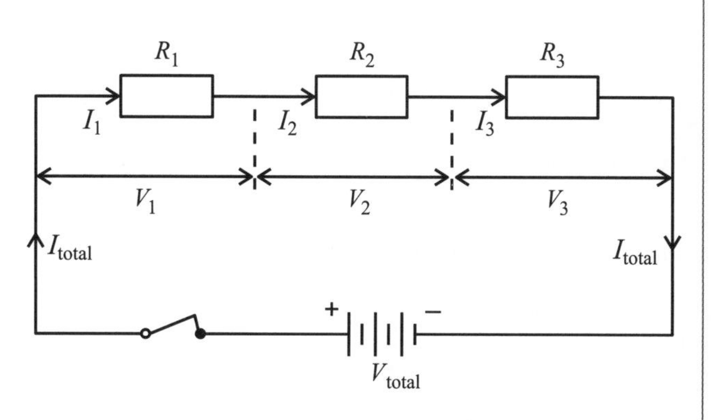

LEGEND

V_{total} = terminal voltage or total potential difference of the energy source (battery in this case)

I_{total} = total current drawn from the supply (note the direction of flow)

R_1, R_2 and R_3 = the three resistances connected in series

I_1 = current flowing through R_1

I_2 = current flowing through R_2

I_3 = current flowing through R_3

V_1 = voltage drop across R_1

V_2 = voltage drop across R_2

V_3 = voltage drop across R_3

Figure 4.8: Resistors in series

Important formulae for resistors in series

The following are important formulae for resistors in series, as shown in Figure 4.8:

- **Total current**
  $I_{total} = I_1 = I_2 = I_3$
  This means that the total current (I_{total}) drawn from the supply is the same as the current that flows through R_1 in the form of I_1, through R_2 in the form of I_2 and through R_3in the form of I_3.
- **Total potential difference**
  $V_{total} = V_1 + V_2 + V_3$
  This means that the potential difference across the supply is equal to the sum of the voltage drops across each series-connected resistor. Resistors connected in series are **electrical potential (voltage) dividers.**
- **Total resistance**
  $V_{total} = V_1 + V_2 + V_3$

  Applying Ohm's law, we get:

  $$I_{total}R_{total} = I_1R_1 + I_2R_2 + I_3R_3$$

  $$= I_{total}R_1 + I_{total}R_2 + I_{total}R_3 \qquad \text{[Because } I_1 = I_2 = I_3 = I_{total}\text{]}$$

  $$= I_{total}(R_1 + R_2 + R_3)$$

  $$\therefore R_{total} = R_1 + R_2 + R_3 \qquad \text{[Divide both sides by } I_{total}\text{]}$$

  This means that the total resistance of resistors connected in series is simply the sum of their resistances.

Important

- **Voltage drop** is the electrical potential measured across any resistor or ***load***. It is calculated using the formula:

  $V = IR$

  where:
  - V = voltage drop across the resistor in volts (V).
  - I = current flowing through the resistor in amperes (A).
  - R = resistance of the resistor or load in ohms (Ω).
- Note the confusion that the symbol V can cause. It is used to represent all of the following:
  - Voltage, which is the common name given to electrical potential.
  - Potential difference, which is the electrical potential (voltage) measured across the energy source in a closed circuit.
  - Terminal voltage, which is another name for potential difference.
  - Voltage drop, which is the electrical potential across any load or resistor.
- We represent a load such as a light bulb, kettle, geyser, toaster and electric iron in a circuit as a simple resistor.

load: *an electrical component or portion of a circuit that consumes electrical power*

Example 4.8

Three resistors of 12 Ω, 7 Ω and 5 Ω are connected in series across a 120 V supply.

Calculate the following:

1. Total resistance of the circuit.
2. Total current flow through the circuit.
3. Current flow through each resistor.
4. Voltage drop across each resistor.
5. Power drawn from the supply.
6. Energy dissipated by the circuit in 20 seconds.

Solution

Given: $V_{total} = 120$ V $\quad R_1 = 12\ \Omega \quad R_2 = 7\ \Omega \quad R_3 = 5\ \Omega$

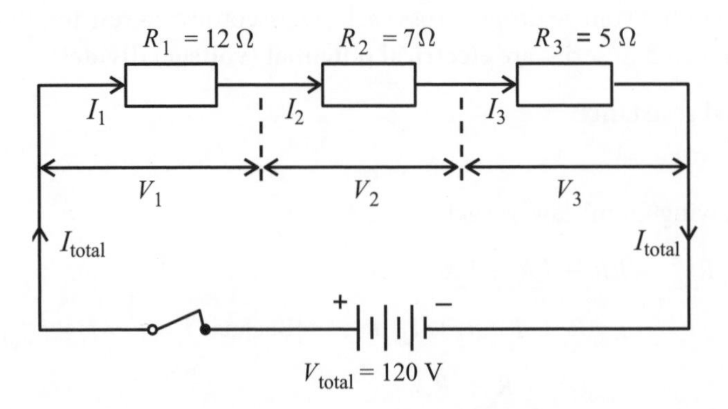

Figure 4.9: Circuit diagram for Example 4.8

Exam tip

- Always draw a large, neat circuit diagram.
- Label the potential difference of the supply, all currents and all voltage drops.
- Choose the correct formula.
- Show the substitution.
- Include the unit of measurement in your answer.

1. $R_{total} = R_1 + R_2 + R_3$
$= 12 + 7 + 5$
$= 24\ \Omega$

2. $I_{total} = \dfrac{V_{total}}{R_{total}}$
$= \dfrac{120}{24}$
$= 5\ A$

3. $I_1 = I_2 = I_3 = I_{total} = 5\ A$

4. $V_1 = I_1R_1 = (5)(12) = 60\ V$
$V_2 = I_2R_2 = (5)(7) = 35\ V$
$V_3 = I_3R_3 = (5)(5) = 25\ V$

5. $P_{total} = V_{total}I_{total} = (120)(5) = 600\ W$
or
$P_{total} = I^2_{total}R_{total} = (5)^2(24) = 600\ W$
or
$P_{total} = \dfrac{V^2_{total}}{R_{total}} = \dfrac{120^2}{24} = 600\ W$

6. $Q = Pt = (600)(20) = 12\ 000\ J$
or
$Q = I^2Rt = (5)^2(24)(20) = 12\ 000\ J$
or
$Q = VIt = (120)(5)(20) = 12\ 000\ J$

Example 4.9

Two resistors connected in series draw 3,6 A of current from the supply. The voltage drop across the first resistor is 45 V and the power drawn by the second resistor is 60 W.

Calculate:

1. The resistance of each resistor.
2. The supply voltage.
3. The energy dissipated in the circuit in 5 minutes.

Solution

Given: $I_{total} = 3,6\ A$ $V_1 = 45\ V$ $P_2 = 60\ W$ $t = 5$ minutes

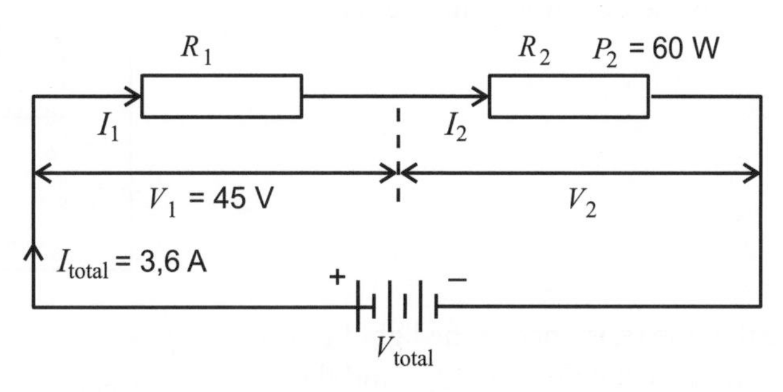

Figure 4.10: Circuit diagram for Example 4.9

1. $I_1 = I_2 = I_{total} = 3{,}6$ A

$V_1 = I_1 R_1$

$R_1 = \frac{V_1}{I_1}$

$= \frac{45}{3{,}6}$

$= 12{,}5\ \Omega$

$P_2 = I_2^2 R_2$

$R_2 = \frac{P_2}{I_2^2}$

$= \frac{60}{(3{,}6)^2}$

$= 4{,}63\ \Omega$

2. $R_{total} = R_1 + R_2$

$= (12{,}5 + 4{,}63)$

$= 17{,}13\ \Omega$

$V_{total} = I_{total} R_{total}$

$= (3{,}6)(17{,}13)$

$= 61{,}668$ V

or

$V_2 = I_2 R_2$

$= (3{,}6)(4{,}63)$

$= 16{,}668$ V

$V_{total} = V_1 + V_2$

$= 45 + 16{,}668$

$= 61{,}668$ V

3. $Q = V_{total} I_{total} t$

$= (61{,}668)(3{,}6)(5 \times 60)$

$= 66\ 601{,}44$ J

or

$Q = I_{total}^2 R_{total} t$

$= (3{,}6)^2(17{,}13)(5 \times 60)$

$= 66\ 601{,}44$ J

Example 4.10

A 12 V light bulb rated at 60 W must be used in a 24 V circuit. Using simple calculations, show how this is possible.

Solution

Given: $V_{original} = 12$ V $V_{new} = 24$ V $P = 60$ W

Note that the light bulb is represented by a simple resistor.

$I_1 = \frac{P}{V} = \frac{60}{12} = 5$ A

$V_1 = V_{total} = 12$ V

$R = \frac{V_1}{I_1} = \frac{12}{5} = 2{,}4\ \Omega$

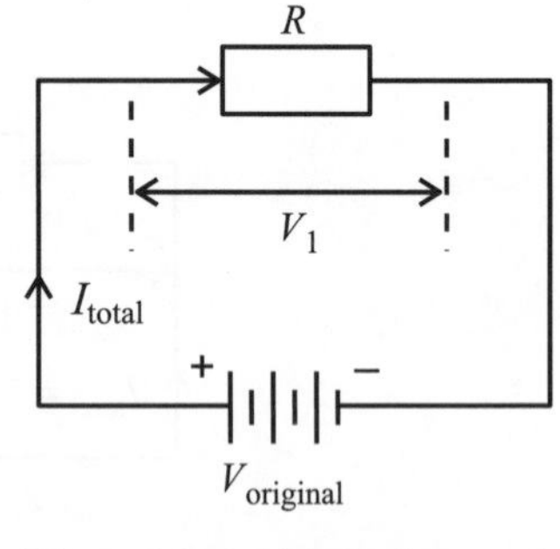

Figure 4.11a: Circuit diagram for Example 4.10

These calculations show that the resistance of the light bulb is 2,4 Ω, the voltage drop across the light bulb is 12 V and the maximum current through the light bulb should not exceed 5 A.

$I_{total} = \frac{V_{new}}{R}$

$= \frac{24}{2{,}4}$

$= 10$ A

This calculation shows that current is now more than the maximum current that should flow through the light bulb. The light bulb will be very bright for a very short period and then it will blow (stop working). To prevent this from happening, the current of 5 A must be maintained.

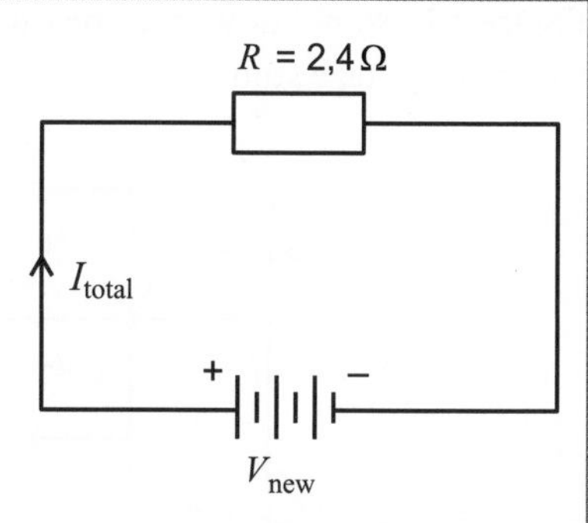

Figure 4.11b: Circuit diagram for Example 4.10

$$\therefore R_{total} = \frac{V_{new}}{I} = \frac{24}{5} = 4{,}8\ \Omega$$

This calculation shows that the total resistance of the circuit must be increased to 4,8 Ω by connecting a 2,4 Ω resistor in series with the light bulb.

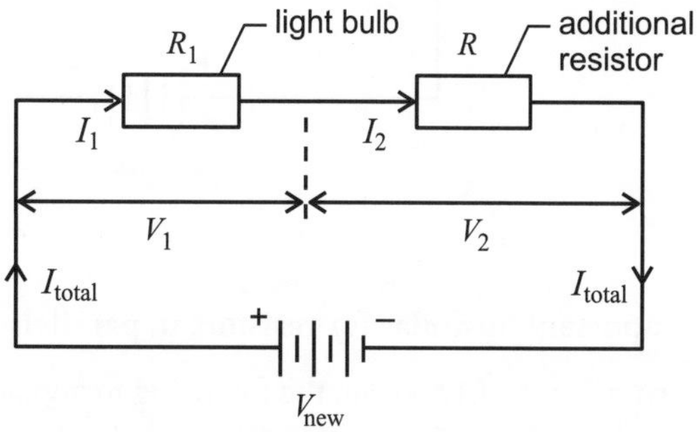

Figure 4.11c: Circuit diagram for Example 4.10

$R_{total} = R_1 + R_2 = 4{,}8\ \Omega$

$$I_{total} = \frac{V_{new}}{R_{total}} = \frac{24}{4{,}8} = 5\ \text{A}$$

$$V_1 = I_1 R_1 = (5)(2{,}4) = 12\ \text{V}$$

$$V_2 = I_2 R_2 = (5)(2{,}4) = 12\ \text{V}$$

The additional resistor made the following possible:

- The current is reduced from 10 A to 5 A.
- The voltage drop across the light bulb is 12 V again.

Therefore, this light bulb can be used in a 24 V circuit.

4.2.2 Resistors connected in parallel

Figure 4.12 shows how three resistors are connected in parallel and across a common voltage source.

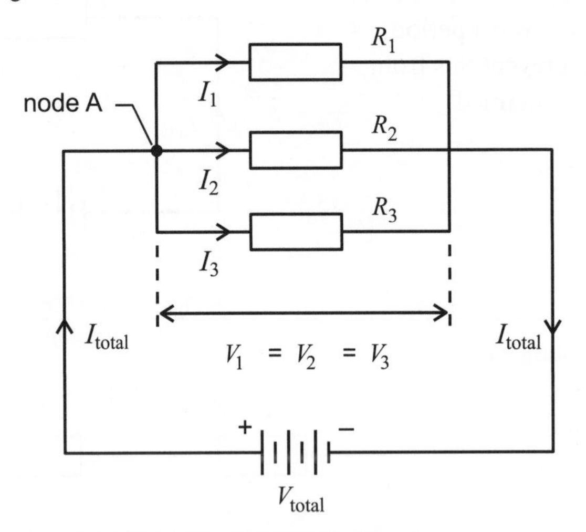

Figure 4.12: Resistors connected in parallel

Important formulae for resistors in parallel

From Figure 4.12 we get the following formulae:

- **Total current**

  $I_{total} = I_1 + I_2 + I_3$

  This means that the total current flowing towards node A is equal to the sum of the three currents flowing in each branch of the parallel circuit. Resistors connected in parallel are **current dividers.**
- **Total potential difference**

  $V_{total} = V_1 = V_2 = V_3$

  This means that the voltage drops across parallel-connected resistors are equal and also equal to the potential difference of the supply.
- **Total resistance**

  $I_{total} = I_1 + I_2 + I_3$

  Applying Ohm's law, we get:

  $$\frac{V_{total}}{R_{total}} = \frac{V_1}{R_1} + \frac{V_2}{R_2} + \frac{V_3}{R_3}$$

  $$= \frac{V_{total}}{R_1} + \frac{V_{total}}{R_2} + \frac{V_{total}}{R_3} \text{ [Because } V_{total} = V_1 = V_2 = V_3\text{]}$$

  $$= V_{total}\left[\frac{1}{R_1} + \frac{1}{R_2} + \frac{1}{R_3}\right]$$

  $$\therefore \frac{1}{R_{total}} = \frac{1}{R_1} + \frac{1}{R_2} + \frac{1}{R_3} \text{ [Divide both sides by } V_{total}\text{]}$$

Exam tip

When you use the formula $\frac{1}{R_{total}} = \frac{1}{R_1} + \frac{1}{R_2} + \frac{1}{R_3}$, it can become quite difficult to determine the lowest common denominator in order to add the fractions on the right-hand side.

Let us look at an alternative:

$$\frac{1}{R_{total}} = \frac{1}{R_1} + \frac{1}{R_2} + \frac{1}{R_3}$$

$$= \frac{R_2R_3 + R_1R_3 + R_1R_2}{R_1R_2R_3} \qquad \text{[Let the common denominator be } R_1R_2R_3\text{]}$$

$$R_{total} = \frac{R_1R_2R_3}{R_1R_2 + R_1R_3 + R_2R_3}$$

We can do the same for **two resistors** in parallel:

$$\frac{1}{R_{total}} = \frac{1}{R_1} + \frac{1}{R_2}$$

$$= \frac{R_2 + R_1}{R_1R_2}$$

$$R_{total} = \frac{R_1R_2}{R_1 + R_2}$$

Example 4.11

Two resistors of 20 Ω and 30 Ω are connected in parallel to a 100 V supply.

Calculate:

1. The total resistance of the circuit.
2. The total current drawn from the supply.
3. The voltage drop across each resistor.
4. The current flow through each resistor.
5. The total power drawn from the supply.

Solution

Given: $R_1 = 20\ \Omega$ $\qquad R_2 = 30\ \Omega$ $\qquad V_{total} = 100\ \text{V}$

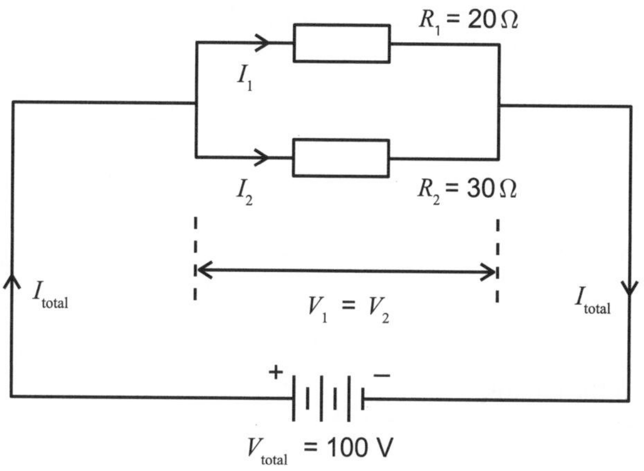

Figure 4.13: Circuit diagram for Example 4.11

1. $\frac{1}{R_{total}} = \frac{1}{R_1} + \frac{1}{R_2}$

$= \frac{1}{20} + \frac{1}{30}$

$= \frac{3 + 2}{60}$

$= \frac{5}{60}$

$R_{total} = \frac{60}{5}$

$= 12\ \Omega$

or

$R_{total} = \frac{R_1 R_2}{R_1 + R_2}$

$= \frac{(20)(30)}{20 + 30}$

$= \frac{600}{50}$

$= 12\ \Omega$

2. $I_{total} = \frac{V_{total}}{R_{total}}$

$= \frac{100}{12}$

$= 8{,}333\ A$

3. $V_1 = V_2 = V_{total} = 100\ V$

4. $I_1 = \frac{V_1}{R_1}$

$= \frac{100}{20}$

$= 5\ A$

$I_2 = \frac{V_2}{R_2}$

$= \frac{100}{30}$

$= 3{,}333\ A$

5. $P_{total} = V_{total} I_{total}$

$= (100)(8{,}333)$

$= 833{,}3\ W$

or

$P_{total} = I^2_{total} R_{total}$

$= (8{,}333)^2(12)$

$= 833{,}267\ W$

Example 4.12

Three resistors are connected in parallel across an unknown power supply. The current flowing through R_1 and R_3 are 1,5 A and 2A, respectively. R_2 draws 180 W of power and the energy consumed by R_3 in 10 seconds is 1 200 J.

Calculate:

1. The resistance of R_3.
2. The supply voltage.
3. The current flow through R_2.
4. The resistance of R_2.
5. The resistance of R_1.
6. The total resistance of the circuit.

Solution

Given: $I_1 = 1,5$ A $P_2 = 180$ W $Q_3 = 1\ 200$ J $t = 10$ s $I_3 = 2$ A

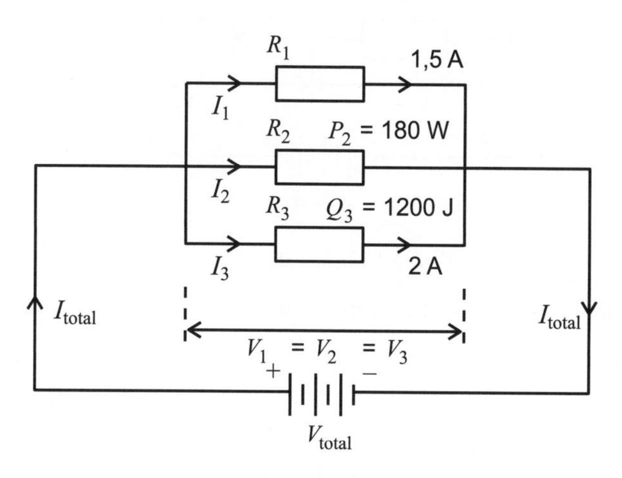

Figure 4.14: Circuit diagram for Example 4.12

1.
$$Q_3 = I_3^2 R_3 t$$
$$I_3^2 R_3 t = Q_3$$
$$R_3 = \frac{Q_3}{I_3^2 t}$$
$$= \frac{1\ 200}{(2)^2(10)}$$
$$= 30\ \Omega$$

2.
$$V_3 = I_3 R_3$$
$$= (2)(30)$$
$$= 60 \text{ V}$$
$$V_1 = V_2 = V_3 = V_{total} = 60 \text{ V}$$

3.
$$P_2 = V_2 I_2$$
$$I_2 = \frac{P_2}{V_2}$$
$$= \frac{180}{60}$$
$$= 3 \text{ A}$$

4.
$$R_2 = \frac{V_2}{I_2}$$
$$= \frac{60}{3}$$
$$= 20\ \Omega$$

5.
$$R_1 = \frac{V_1}{I_1}$$
$$= \frac{60}{1,5}$$
$$= 40\ \Omega$$

6.
$$I_{total} = I_1 + I_2 + I_3$$
$$= 1,5 + 3 + 2$$
$$= 6,5 \text{ A}$$
$$R_{total} = \frac{V_{total}}{I_{total}}$$
$$= \frac{60}{6,5}$$
$$= 9,231\ \Omega$$

or

$$\frac{1}{R_{total}} = \frac{1}{R_1} + \frac{1}{R_2} + \frac{1}{R_3}$$
$$= \frac{1}{40} + \frac{1}{20} + \frac{1}{30}$$
$$= \frac{3 + 6 + 4}{120}$$
$$= \frac{13}{120}$$
$$R_{total} = \frac{120}{13}$$
$$= 9,231\ \Omega$$

or

$$R_{total} = \frac{R_1 R_2 R_3}{R_1 R_2 + R_1 R_3 + R_2 R_3}$$
$$= \frac{(40)(20)(30)}{(40)(20) + (40)(30) + (20)(30)}$$
$$= \frac{24\ 000}{800 + 1\ 200 + 600}$$
$$= \frac{24\ 000}{2\ 600}$$
$$= 9,231\ \Omega$$

Activity 4.3

1. Study Figure 4.15 carefully and then answer the question that follows.

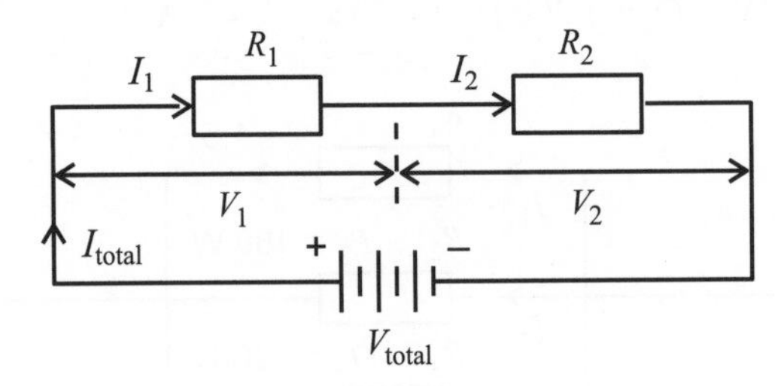

Figure 4.15: Resistors in series

What do each of the following symbols represent?

1.1 V_{total}

1.2 I_1

1.3 V_2 (3 × 1 = 3)

2. State five electrical concepts represented by the symbol *V*. (5)

3. State whether each of the following is true or false. If false, give a reason.

In a circuit containing two resistors in series:

3.1 $R_{total} = R_1 \times R_2$

3.2 $I_{total} = I_1 + I_2$

3.3 $V_{total} = V_1 = V_2$ (3 × 2 = 6)

4. Two resistors of 25 Ω and 40 Ω are connected in series across a 220 V supply.

Calculate:

4.1 The total resistance of the circuit.

4.2 The current drawn from the supply.

4.3 The current flow through each resistor.

4.4 The voltage drop across each resistor.

4.5 The total power drawn by the circuit. (5 × 2 = 10)

5. Two resistors of 60 Ω and 45 Ω are connected in series across a 300 V supply.

Calculate:

5.1 The resistance of a third resistor that must be connected in series with these resistors in order to limit the current to 1,5 A.

5.2 The voltage drop across the third resistor. (2 × 2 = 4)

6. State whether each of the following is true or false. If false, give a reason.

In a circuit containing two resistors in parallel:

6.1 $V_{total} = V_1 + V_2$ (2)

6.2 $I_{total} = I_1 = I_2$ (2)

6.3 $\frac{1}{R_{total}} = \frac{1}{R_1} + \frac{1}{R_2}$ (1)

6.4 $R_{total} = \frac{R_1 + R_2}{R_1 R_2}$ (2)

7. A circuit supplied by 90 V has three resistors of 10 Ω, 15 Ω and 25 Ω. Calculate the total current flowing through the circuit if:

   7.1 The resistors are connected in series.

   7.2 The resistors are connected in parallel. (2 × 4 = 8)

8. Three resistors of 40 Ω, 50 Ω and 60 Ω are connected in parallel across a 250 V supply. Calculate:

   8.1 The total resistance of the circuit. (2)

   8.2 The total current drawn by the circuit. (2)

   8.3 The voltage drop across each resistor. (2)

   8.4 The current flow through each resistor. (6)

   8.5 The power drawn by the 50 Ω resistor. (2)

   8.6 The energy dissipated by the circuit in 55 seconds. (3)

9. Two resistors are connected in parallel and draw 4,7 A from the supply. The power drawn by R_1 is 240 W and the current drawn by R_2 is 2,2 A. Calculate:

   9.1 The current flow through R_1. (2)

   9.2 The potential difference of the supply. (2)

   9.3 The voltage drop across each resistor. (2)

   9.4 The resistance of each resistor. (4)

10. The total current drawn from a 280 V supply is 7 A. There are three resistors connected in series. Calculate the resistance of R_3 if the resistances of the other two resistors are 13 Ω and 17 Ω. (5)

TOTAL: [75]

4.2.3 Series-parallel circuits

These circuits are a little more challenging, because current and voltage are divided in the same circuit.

Deal with these circuits in the following way:

Step 1	Draw a large circuit diagram.
Step 2	Label all resistors.
Step 3	Indicate all currents and voltage drops.
Step 4	Indicate the potential difference of the source and the total current of the circuit.
Step 5	Solve the circuit by starting with the part of the circuit where the most information is given.

Example 4.13

Two resistors of 24 Ω and 40 Ω are connected in parallel. This parallel combination is then connected in series with a 10 Ω resistor. The circuit is connected to a 200 V supply.

Calculate:

1. The resistance of the parallel combination.
2. The total resistance of the circuit.
3. The total current drawn from the supply.
4. The voltage drop across the parallel combination.
5. The current flow through each resistor.
6. The power drawn by the 24 Ω resistor.

Solution

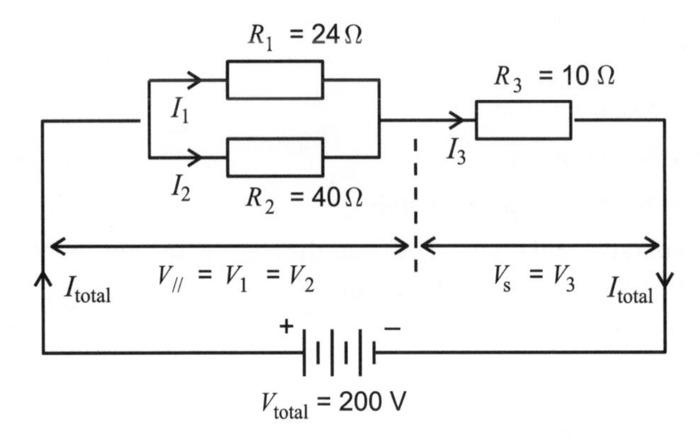

Figure 4.16: Circuit diagram for Example 4.13

Note

We use the subscript '//' to represent the parallel combination.
We use the subscript 'S' to refer to a series combination.

1. $R_{//} = \frac{R_1 R_2}{R_1 + R_2}$

$= \frac{(24)(40)}{24 + 40}$

$= 15\ \Omega$

2. $R_{total} = R_{//} + R_3$

$= 15 + 10$

$= 25\ \Omega$

3. $I_{total} = \frac{V_{total}}{R_{total}}$

$= \frac{200}{25}$

$= 8\ \text{A}$

4. $I_{total} = I_3 = 8\ \text{A}$

$V_3 = I_3 R_3$

$= (8)(10)$

$= 80\ \text{V}$

$\therefore V_{//} = V_{total} - V_3$

$= 200 - 80$

$= 120\ \text{V}$

or

$V_{//} = I_{//} R_{//}$

$= (8)(15)$ $\quad [I_{//} = I_{total}]$

$= 120\ \text{V}$

5. $I_3 = I_{total}$

$V_{//} = V_1 = V_2$

$I_1 = \frac{V_1}{R_1}$

$= \frac{120}{24}$

$= 5\ A$

$I_2 = \frac{V_2}{R_2}$

$= \frac{120}{40}$

$= 3\ A$

6. $P_1 = I_1^2 R_1$

$= (5)^2(24)$

$= 600\ W$

or

$P_1 = V_1 I_1$

$= (120)(5)$

$= 600\ W$

Example 4.14

A 15 Ω resistor is connected in series with a 30 Ω resistor. This series combination is then connected in parallel with a 20 Ω resistor across a 60 V supply.

Calculate:

1. The total resistance of the circuit.
2. The total current drawn from the supply.
3. The current drawn by each resistor.
4. The voltage drop across each resistor.
5. The energy dissipated by the circuit in 5 minutes. Give your answer in kJ.

Solution

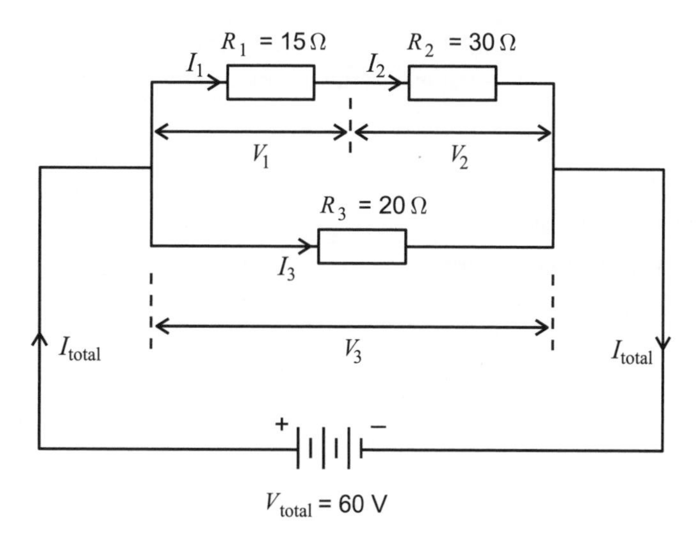

Figure 4.17: Circuit diagram for Example 4.14

1. $R_S = R_1 + R_2$
$= 15 + 30$
$= 45\ \Omega$
$R_{total} = \frac{R_S R_3}{R_S + R_3}$
$= \frac{(45)(20)}{45 + 20}$
$= 13{,}846\ \Omega$

2. $I_{total} = \frac{V_{total}}{R_{total}}$
$= \frac{60}{13{,}846}$
$= 4{,}333\ A$

3. $V_3 = V_{total} = 60\ V$
$I_3 = \frac{V_3}{R_3}$
$= \frac{60}{20}$
$= 3\ A$
$I_1 = I_2 = I_{total} - I_3$
$= 4{,}333 - 3$
$= 1{,}333\ A$

4. $V_3 = V_{total} = 60\ V$
$V_1 = I_1 R_1$
$= (1{,}333)(15)$
$= 19{,}995\ V$
$V_2 = I_2 R_2$
$= (1{,}333)(30)$
$= 39{,}99\ V$

5. $Q = I^2_{total} R_{total} t$
$= (4{,}333)^2(13{,}846)(5 \times 60)$
$= 77\ 987{,}134\ J$
$= 77{,}987\ kJ$

Example 4.15

Two resistors of 18 Ω and 24 Ω are connected in series. This series combination is then connected in parallel with a 5 Ω resistor and a 10 Ω resistor in series across a 150 V supply.

Calculate:

1. The total resistance of the circuit.
2. The current drawn from the supply.
3. The current flow through each resistor.
4. The voltage drop across each resistor.

Solution

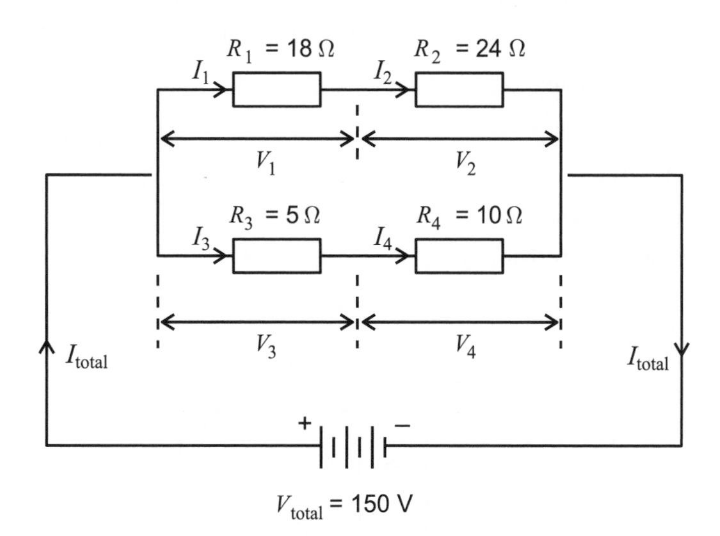

Figure 4.18: Circuit diagram for Example 4.15

1. $R_{S1} = R_1 + R_2$ [R_{S1} = resistance of series resistors 1]

$= 18 + 24$

$= 42\ \Omega$

$R_{S2} = R_3 + R_4$ [R_{S2} = resistance of series resistors 2]

$= 5 + 10$

$= 15\ \Omega$

$$R_{total} = \frac{R_{S1}R_{S2}}{R_{S1} + R_{S2}}$$

$$= \frac{(42)(15)}{42 + 15}$$

$$= 11{,}053\ \Omega$$

2. $$I_{total} = \frac{V_{total}}{R_{total}}$$

$$= \frac{150}{11{,}053}$$

$$= 13{,}571\ \text{A}$$

3. $V_{S1} = V_1 + V_2 = V_{total}$

$V_{S2} = V_3 + V_4 = V_{total}$

$$I_{S1} = \frac{V_{S1}}{R_{S1}} = \frac{150}{42} = 3{,}571\ \text{A} = I_1 = I_2$$

$$I_{S2} = \frac{V_{S2}}{R_{S2}} = \frac{150}{15} = 10\ \text{A} = I_3 = I_4$$

4. $V_1 = I_1R_1 = (3{,}571)(18) = 64{,}278\ \text{V}$

$V_2 = I_2R_2 = (3{,}571)(24) = 85{,}704\ \text{V}$

$V_3 = I_3R_3 = (10)(5) = 50\ \text{V}$

$V_4 = I_4R_4 = (10)(10) = 100\ \text{V}$

Example 4.16

A 50 Ω resistor is connected in parallel with a 20 Ω resistor. This parallel combination is then connected in series with another parallel combination of a 70 Ω resistor and a 35 Ω resistor.

If the supply voltage is 220 V, calculate:

1. The total resistance of the circuit.
2. The total current of the circuit.
3. The voltage drop across each resistor.
4. The current flow through each resistor.

Solution

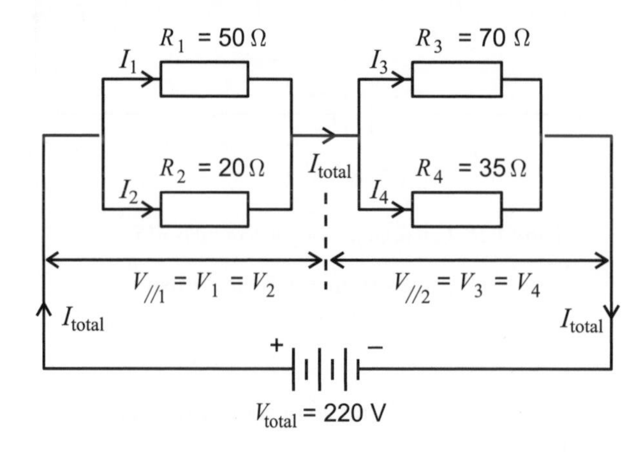

Figure 4.19: Circuit diagram for Example 4.16

1. $R_{//1} = \frac{R_1 R_2}{R_1 + R_2} = \frac{(50)(20)}{50 + 20} = 14{,}286\ \Omega$

$R_{//2} = \frac{R_3 R_4}{R_3 + R_4} = \frac{70 \times 35}{70 + 35} = 23{,}333\ \Omega$

$R_{total} = R_{//1} + R_{//2} = 14{,}286 + 23{,}333 = 37{,}619\ \Omega$

2. $I_{total} = \frac{V_{total}}{R_{total}} = \frac{220}{37{,}619} = 5{,}848\ \text{A}$

3. $V_{//1} = V_1 = V_2 = I_{total} \cdot R_{//_1} = (5{,}848)(14{,}286) = 83{,}545\ \text{V}$

$V_{//2} = V_3 = V_4 = I_{total} R_{//2} = (5{,}848)(23{,}333) = 136{,}451\ \text{V}$

4. $I_1 = \frac{V_1}{R_1} = \frac{83{,}545}{50} = 1{,}671\ \text{A}$

$I_2 = \frac{V_2}{R_2} = \frac{83{,}545}{20} = 4{,}177\ \text{A}$

$I_3 = \frac{V_3}{R_3} = \frac{136{,}451}{70} = 1{,}949\ \text{A}$

$I_4 = \frac{V_4}{R_4} = \frac{136{,}451}{35} = 3{,}899\ \text{A}$

Activity 4.4

1. Two resistors of 40 Ω and 60 Ω are connected in parallel. This parallel combination is then connected in series with an unknown resistor. The voltage drop across the unknown resistor is 70 V. If the circuit draws 3,5 A of current from the supply, calculate:
   - 1.1 The unknown resistance. (2)
   - 1.2 The resistance of the parallel combination. (2)
   - 1.3 The total resistance of the circuit. (2)
   - 1.4 The voltage drop across the parallel combination. (2)
   - 1.5 The supply voltage. (2)
   - 1.6 The current flow through each resistor. (5)
   - 1.7 The power drawn by the 60 Ω resistor. (2)
2. A 50 Ω resistor is connected in series with a 35 Ω resistor. This series combination is then connected in parallel with a 60 Ω resistor across a 240 V supply. Calculate:
   - 2.1 The total resistance of the circuit. (4)
   - 2.2 The total current drawn from the supply. (2)
   - 2.3 The current flow through each resistor. (5)
   - 2.4 The voltage drop across each resistor. (5)
   - 2.5 The energy dissipated by the circuit in 2,5 minutes. (3)
3. An electric circuit has two series combinations connected in parallel with each other. The first series combination has a 100 Ω resistor and a 40 Ω resistor. The second series combination has a 48 Ω resistor and a 32 Ω resistor. For a supply voltage of 200 V, calculate:
   - 3.1 The total resistance of the circuit. (4)
   - 3.2 The total current flowing through the circuit. (2)
   - 3.3 The current flow through each resistor. (5)
   - 3.4 The voltage drop across each resistor. (8)

TOTAL: [55]

Unit 4.3: Factors influencing the resistance of a conductor

cross-sectional area: *area of the surface exposed by making a straight perpendicular slice through a three-dimensional object*

resistivity: *the resistance offered by a conductor because of the type of material it is made of*

The resistance of any conductor is influenced by the following factors:

- Length.
- ***Cross-sectional area.***
- ***Resistivity.***
- Temperature.

4.3.1 Length

The resistance of a conductor is directly proportional to its length. This means that the longer the conductor, the higher its resistance.

Length is represented by the symbol l and is measured in metres (m).

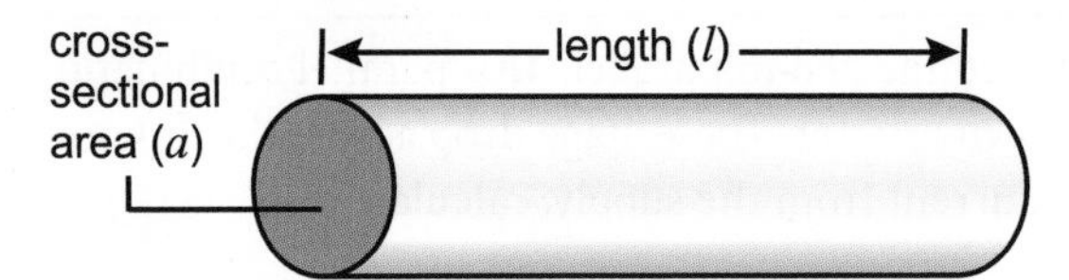

Figure 4.20: Length and cross-sectional area of a conductor

4.3.2 Cross-sectional area

The resistance of any conductor is inversely proportional to its cross-sectional area. This means that the bigger the area, the smaller the resistance.

Cross-sectional area is represented by the symbol a and is measured in square metres (m^2).

Formulae to calculate the cross-sectional area of a round object

To calculate the cross-sectional area of a round conductor, we use one of the following formulae:

- $a = \pi r^2$
- $a = \frac{\pi d^2}{4}$

where:

- a = cross-sectional area in square metres (m^2).
- r = radius of the conductor in metres (m).
- d = diameter of the conductor in metres (m).

Exam tip

Converting between units

Students often find it difficult to convert from one unit to another. Table 4.2 will help you with conversions using the base unit metres. You can also use this table for conversions of any other base unit, for example joules or watts.

Table 4.2: Converting units of measurement

Units	Length (l)	Area (a)	Volume (v)		
	(m^1)	(m^2)	(m^3)	÷	×
mm (millimetre)				× 10–(sum of indices) ↑	× 10+(sum of indices) ↓
	10^1	10^2	10^3		
cm (centimetre)					
	10^1	10^2	10^3		
dm (decimetre)					
	10^1	10^2	10^3		
m (metre)					
	10^1	10^2	10^3		
dam (decametre)					
	10^1	10^2	10^3		
hm (hectometre)					
	10^1	10^2	10^3		
km (kilometre)					

1. To write down the units in the correct order, use this mnemonic: (m)y (c)at (d)rinks (m)ilk, (d)ogs (h)ate (k)ittens

2. Convert 185 mm to m:

   185 mm $= 185 \times 10^{-(1+1+1)}$ [Convert from smaller to larger unit ∴ index is negative]

   $= 185 \times 10^{-3}$ m [Add indices in 'length' column]

   $= 0{,}185$ m

3. Convert 2,5 km to m:

   2,5 km $= 2{,}5 \times 10^{+(1+1+1)}$ [Larger unit to smaller unit ∴ index is positive]

   $= 2{,}5 \times 10^{3}$ m [Add indices in 'length' column]

   $= 2\ 500$ m

4. Convert 250 mm^2 to m^2:

   250 mm^2 $= 250 \times 10^{-(2+2+2)}$

   $= 250 \times 10^{-6}$ m^2 [Smaller unit to larger unit ∴ index is negative]

   $= 0{,}000250$ m^2 [Add indices in 'area' column]

5. Convert 5 m^3 to cm^3:

   5 m^3 $= 5 \times 10^{+(3+3)}$ [Larger unit to smaller unit ∴ index is positive]

   $= 5 \times 10^{6}$ cm^3 [Add indices in 'volume' column]

   $= 5\ 000\ 000$ cm^3

6. For a table of prefixes, see Table 4.3.

Table 4.3: Prefixes used with electrical quantities

Prefix	Denoted as	Meaning
milli-	1 mΩ = 1 milli-ohm	1×10^{-3} Ω
micro-	1 μΩ = 1 micro-ohm	1×10^{-6} Ω
nano-	1 nΩ = 1 nano-ohm	1×10^{-9} Ω
pico-	1 pΩ = 1 pico-ohm	1×10^{-12} Ω

Example 4.17

1. Convert:
   - 1.1 4,5 mm to m.
   - 1.2 6 mm to m.
   - 1.3 5 cm to m.
   - 1.4 20 km to m.
   - 1.5 425 mm^2 to m^2.
   - 1.6 60 cm^2 to m^2.
   - 1.7 2,5 μΩm to Ωm.
   - 1.8 5,71 μΩm to Ωm.
2. Calculate the cross-sectional area of a conductor in m^2 if:
   - 2.1 $r = 2{,}5$ mm.
   - 2.2 $r = 8$ cm.
   - 2.3 $d = 18$ mm.
   - 2.4 $d = 9{,}5$ cm.

Solution

1.1 $4{,}5 \times 10^{-(1+1+1)}$

$= 4{,}5 \times 10^{-3}$ m or 0,0045 m

1.2 $6 \times 10^{-(1+1+1)}$

$= 6 \times 10^{-3}$ m or 0,006 m

1.3 $5 \times 10^{-(1+1)}$

$= 5 \times 10^{-2}$ m or 0,05 m

1.4 $20 \times 10^{+(1+1+1)}$

$= 20 \times 10^{3}$ m or 20 000 m

1.5 $425 \times 10^{-(2+2+2)}$

$= 425 \times 10^{-6}$ m^2 or 0,000425 m^2

1.6 $60 \times 10^{-(2+2)}$

$= 60 \times 10^{-4}$ m^2 or 0,006 m^2

1.7 2,5 μΩ m

$= 2,5 \times 10^{-6}\ \Omega$ m

1.8 5,71 μΩ m

$= 5,71 \times 10^{-6}\ \Omega$ m

2.1 $r = 2,5$ mm $= 2,5 \times 10^{-3}$ m

$a = \pi r^2$

$= \pi(2,5 \times 10^{-3})^2$

$= 1,963 \times 10^{-5}$ m^2

2.2 $r = 8$ cm $= 8 \times 10^{-2}$ m

$a = \pi r^2$

$= \pi(8 \times 10^{-2})^2$

$= 20,106 \times 10^{-3}$ m^2

2.3 $d = 18$ mm $= 18 \times 10^{-3}$ m

$a = \frac{\pi d^2}{4}$

$= \frac{\pi(18 \times 10^{-3})^2}{4}$

$= 2,545 \times 10^{-4}$ m^2

2.4 $d = 9,5$ cm $= 9,5 \times 10^{-2}$ m

$a = \frac{\pi d^2}{4}$

$= \frac{\pi(9,5 \times 10^{-2})^2}{4}$

$= 7,088 \times 10^{-3}$ m^2

4.3.3 Resistivity

Resistivity is a property of materials. This property means that materials oppose current flow.

Resistivity

Resistivity is defined as the resistance between the opposite faces of a 1 metre cube of that material.

Simply put, resistivity is the resistance offered by a material due to the type (nature) of the material. Resistivity is also known as *specific resistance.*

Resistivity is represented by the symbol ρ (rho) and is measured in ohm metres (Ω m).

Formula for calculating the resistance of a conductor provided temperature remains constant

The resistance of any conductor is calculated using the following formula. Note that the temperature must remain constant.

$$R = \frac{\rho l}{a}$$

where:

- R = resistance in ohms (Ω).
- l = length in metres (m).
- a = cross-sectional area in square metres (m^2).
- ρ = resistivity in ohm metres (Ω m).

Example 4.18

Calculate the resistance of a copper conductor that is 3,2 km long with a diameter of 4 mm. Take the resistivity of copper to be 0,0168 μΩ m.

Solution

Given:

$l = 3{,}2 \text{ km} = 3{,}2 \times 10^3$ or 3 200 m

$\rho = 0{,}0168 \ \mu\Omega \text{ m} = 0{,}0168 \times 10^{-6} \ \Omega \text{ m}$

$d = 4 \text{ mm} = 4 \times 10^{-3} \text{ m}$

$$a = \frac{\pi d^2}{4}$$

$$= \frac{\pi(4 \times 10^{-3})^2}{4}$$

$$= 1{,}257 \times 10^{-5} \text{ m}^2$$

$$R = \frac{\rho l}{a}$$

$$= \frac{(0{,}0168 \times 10^{-6})(3\,200)}{1{,}257 \times 10^{-5}}$$

$$= 4{,}277 \ \Omega$$

> **Note**
>
> Refer to Table 4.3 for the index that applies to conversions for micro units.

Example 4.19

Calculate the length of a copper conductor with a cross-sectional area of 16 mm² and a resistance of 0,75 Ω. The resistivity of copper is 0,0168 μΩ m.

Solution

Given:

$a = 16 \text{ mm}^2 = 16 \times 10^{-6} \text{ m}^2$

$\rho = 0{,}0168 \ \mu\Omega \text{ m} = 0{,}0168 \times 10^{-6} \ \Omega \text{ m}$

$R = 0{,}75 \ \Omega$

$$R = \frac{\rho l}{a}$$

$$\rho l = aR$$

$$l = \frac{aR}{\rho}$$

$$= \frac{(16 \times 10^{-6})(0{,}75)}{0{,}0168 \times 10^{-6}}$$

$$= 714{,}286 \text{ m}$$

Example 4.20

An aluminium conductor has a length of 485 m and a resistance of 2,5 Ω. Calculate the diameter of the conductor if its resistivity is 0,0265 μΩ m.

Solution

Given:

$l = 485$ m $\quad R = 2,5\ \Omega$

$\rho = 0,0265\ \mu\Omega\ \text{m} = 0,0265 \times 10^{-6}\ \Omega\ \text{m}$

$$R = \frac{\rho l}{a}$$

$$aR = \rho l$$

$$a = \frac{\rho l}{R}$$

$$= \frac{(0,0265 \times 10^{-6})(485)}{2,5}$$

$$= 5,141 \times 10^{-6}\ \text{m}^2$$

$$a = \frac{\pi d^2}{4}$$

$$\pi d^2 = 4a$$

$$d^2 = \frac{4a}{\pi}$$

$$d = \sqrt{\frac{4a}{\pi}}$$

$$= \sqrt{\frac{4(5,141 \times 10^{-6})}{\pi}}$$

$$= 2,558 \times 10^{-3}\ \text{m}$$

$$= 2,558\ \text{mm}$$

Activity 4.5

1. State four factors that influence the resistance of a conductor. (4)
2. Complete the following table: (8)

Quantity	Symbol	Unit
Resistance		
	ρ	
	a	
Length		

3. Explain what you understand by resistivity. (2)
4. Convert:

4.1	375 mm to m	4.4	120 cm² to m²
4.2	25 km to m	4.5	780 mm² to m²
4.3	58 cm to m	4.6	1,25 μΩ m to Ω m

$(6 \times 1 = 6)$

5. An aluminium conductor that is 256 m long has a cross-sectional area of 2,5 mm². Calculate the resistance of the conductor if the resistivity of aluminium is 0,027 μΩ m. (3)
6. A copper conductor has a diameter of 3,5 mm and a resistance of 1 Ω. Calculate the length of the conductor if the resistivity of copper is 0,017 μΩ m. (4)
7. Calculate the area of a copper conductor with a length of 1 875 m and a resistance of 0,8 Ω. Take the resistivity of copper to be 0,017 μΩ m. (3)

TOTAL: [30]

Important

Alloys experience very little change in resistance with an increase in temperature. (Examples include manganin, constantin and nichrome).

These materials can be used to manufacture resistors.

4.3.4 Temperature

Temperature is the fourth factor that influences the resistance of any material. The resistance of certain materials increases with an increase in temperature, while the resistance of other materials decreases with an increase in temperature. Some materials (***alloys*** such as manganin and nichrome) experience very little change in resistance with an increase in temperature.

Temperature coefficient of resistance

Definition of the temperature coefficient of resistance

The temperature coefficient of resistance is defined as the increase or decrease in resistance per ohm original resistance per degree rise in temperature.

The temperature coefficient of resistance is represented by the symbol α (alpha) and is given as ohm per ohm per degree Celsius (Ω/Ω °C) or simply as per degree Celsius (/°C).

alloy: *a mixture of two or more metals*

electrolyte: *a substance that separates into ions in solution and obtains the capacity to conduct electricity*

- **Positive temperature coefficient of resistance**
  Conductors such as pure metals (silver, copper, gold and aluminium) experience an increase in resistance with an increase in temperature. These materials have a positive temperature coefficient of resistance.
- **Negative temperature coefficient of resistance**
  Carbon, ***electrolytes***, semiconductors (silicon and germanium) and insulators experience a decrease in resistance with an increase in temperature. These materials have a negative temperature coefficient of resistance.

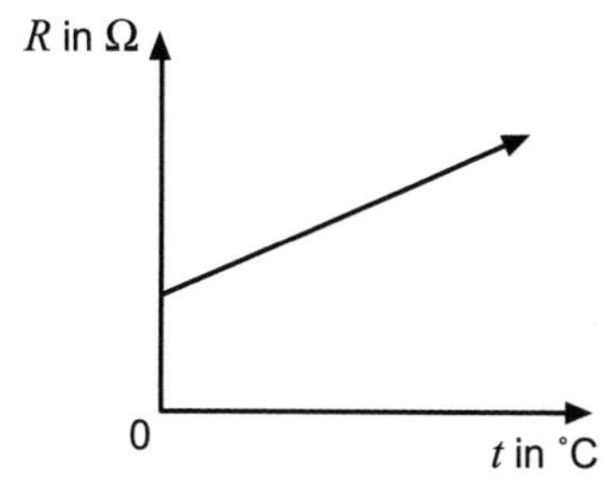

Figure 4.21: Positive temperature coefficient of resistance

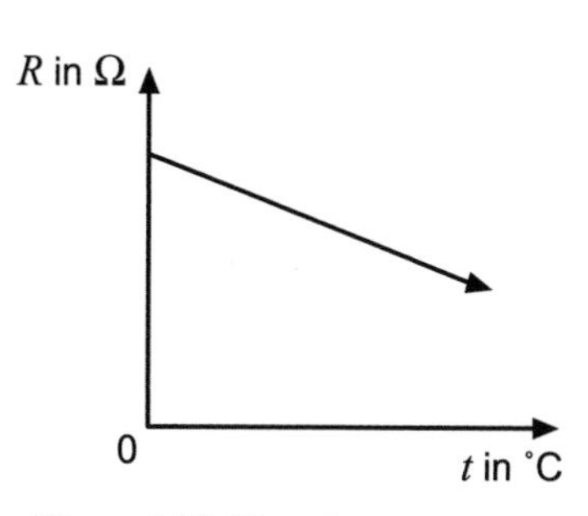

Figure 4.22: Negative temperature coefficient of resistance

Determining the resistance of materials at different temperatures

The standard formula that is used to determine the new resistance of a material when the temperature changes is given by:

$$R_t = R_\theta + R_\theta \alpha_\theta \Delta t$$

where:

- R_t = resistance at a specified temperature (t °C).
- R_θ = resistance at initial temperature (θ °C).
- α_θ = temperature coefficient of resistance at initial temperature (θ °C).
- $\Delta t = (t - \theta)$ = change in temperature, i.e. from the initial temperature (θ) to the specified temperature (t).

From this original formula:

$$R_t = R_\theta + R_\theta \alpha_\theta (t - \theta)$$
$$= R_\theta[1 + \alpha_\theta (t - \theta)]$$

Formula for calculating resistance at a specified temperature when the initial resistance is given at 0° C

$\therefore R_t = R_0[1 + \alpha_0(t - 0)]$

$= R_0(1 + \alpha_0 t)$

where:

- R_t = resistance at a specified temperature (t °C).
- R_0 = resistance at 0 °C.
- α_0 = temperature coefficient of resistance at 0 °C.
- t = specified temperature.

Note

In this syllabus, we do not use the initial temperature (θ); instead we use an initial temperature of 0 °C.

coil: *a length of wire wound in a joined sequence of* **concentric** *rings (turns)*

concentric: *having a common centre*

Example 4.21

The resistance of a wire ***coil*** is 17 Ω at a temperature of 0 °C. Determine the resistance of the coil at 55 °C. Take the temperature coefficient of resistance at 0 °C to be 0,0043/°C.

Solution

Given:

$R_0 = 17\ \Omega$ $\quad t = 55$ °C $\quad \alpha_0 = 0{,}0043$/°C

$R_t = R_0(1 + \alpha_0 t)$

$= 17[1 + (0{,}0043)(55)]$

$= 21{,}021\ \Omega$

Example 4.22

A wire coil has a resistance of 42 Ω at 60 °C. Determine by how much the resistance will decrease if the coil is cooled to 0 °C. Take the temperature coefficient of resistance to be 0,0051/°C at 0 °C.

Solution

Given:

$R_t = 42\ \Omega$ $\quad t = 60$ °C $\quad \alpha_0 = 0{,}0051$/°C

$R_t = R_0(1 + \alpha_0 t)$

$R_0(1 + \alpha_0 t) = R_t$

$R_0 = \frac{R_t}{1 + \alpha_0 t}$

$= \frac{42}{1 + (0{,}0051)(60)}$

$= \frac{42}{1{,}306}$

$= 32{,}159\ \Omega$

The resistance of the coil at 0 °C will be 32,159 Ω.

∴ The resistance will decrease by:

$42 - 32{,}159$

$= 9{,}841\ \Omega$

Activity 4.6

1. Define the temperature coefficient of resistance. (3)
2. Explain what you understand by positive temperature coefficient of resistance. (2)
3. State what will happen to the resistance of each of the following materials as its temperature increases:
   3.1 Aluminium.
   3.2 Copper.
   3.3 Electrolyte.
   3.4 Silicon.
   3.5 Mica.
   3.6 Asbestos.
   3.7 PVC.
   (7 × 1 = 7)
4. State the reason why certain alloys are used in the manufacture of resistors. (2)
5. State what each symbol in the following formula represents:
   $R_t = R_\theta + R_\theta \alpha_\theta \Delta t$ (4)
6. The resistance of a coil of copper wire is 9,5 Ω at 0 °C. Calculate the resistance of this coil at an operating temperature of 40 °C. The temperature coefficient of resistance is 0,004/°C at 0 °C. (4)
7. The ***field coils*** of a motor have a resistance of 20 Ω at 0 °C. Determine the temperature at which these coils will have a resistance of 24 Ω. Take the temperature coefficient of resistance to be 0,0043/°C at 0 °C. (4)
8. The ***windings*** of a motor have a resistance of 13 Ω at 0 °C. Determine by how much the temperature will increase if the resistance of the coils reaches 19 Ω. Take the temperature coefficient of resistance to be 0,005/°C. (4)

TOTAL: [30]

field coils: *insulated copper wire wound round the field poles of a DC motor or generator; also called field windings*

winding: *one or more turns of wire forming a continuous coil through which an electric current can pass*

Unit 4.4: Cells and batteries

The law of conservation of energy

The law of conservation of energy states that:

Energy cannot be created or destroyed, but it can be converted from one form into another.

The greatest challenge in the electrical industry is that electrical energy cannot be stored.

See it online

Law of conservation energy
Learn more in this video – The Law of Conservation of Energy + Forms of Energy by 2 minute classroom | https://youtu.be/_8EEnMwkmZk

Function of cells and batteries

The function of ***cells*** or ***batteries*** is to store chemical energy which will be converted into electrical energy when the cells or batteries are connected in an electric circuit.

cell: *a device that stores chemical energy and converts it into electrical energy*

battery: *two or more identical cells connected together in series or in parallel*

4.4.1 Primary and secondary cells

Primary cells

Definition of primary cell

A primary cell is an energy storage device that creates current flow in a circuit by an irreversible chemical reaction. Primary cells cannot be recharged.

These cells cannot convert electrical energy back into chemical energy. For this reason, primary cells are called single-use, non-rechargeable or 'throw-away' cells or batteries.

The most popular primary cell is the Leclanché cell. These cells are used in torches, cameras, toys, radios, etc. This cell was invented in 1866 by a French engineer, Georges Leclanché.

There are three types of Leclanché cells, namely zinc-carbon, zinc-chloride and alkaline cells.

Table 4.4: Types of primary cells (batteries)

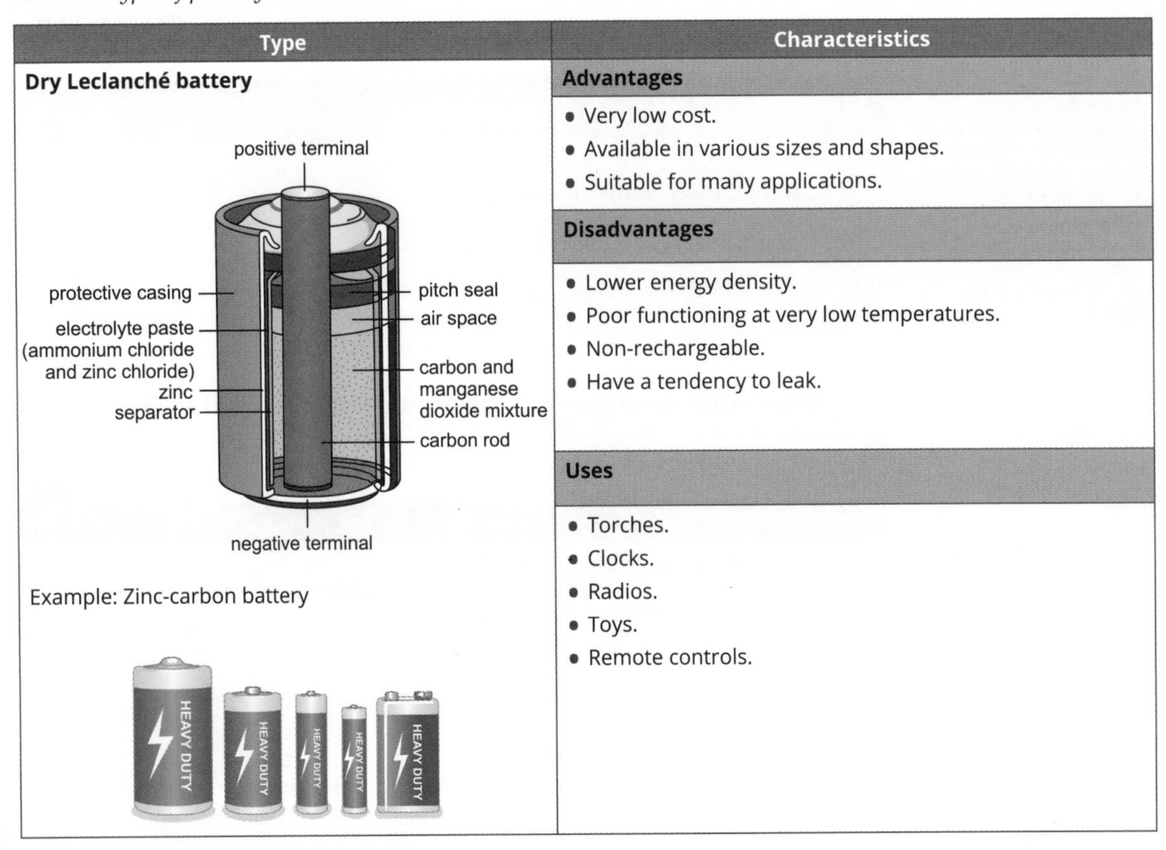

Type	Characteristics
Dry Leclanché battery	**Advantages**
	• Very low cost. • Available in various sizes and shapes. • Suitable for many applications.
	Disadvantages
	• Lower energy density. • Poor functioning at very low temperatures. • Non-rechargeable. • Have a tendency to leak.
	Uses
Example: Zinc-carbon battery	• Torches. • Clocks. • Radios. • Toys. • Remote controls.

Alkaline battery  	**Advantages** • Made from non-toxic materials. • Available in various sizes and shapes. • Reduced chance of leakage. • Very good shelf life. • Suitable for a wide range of applications. **Disadvantages** • Higher cost. • Non-rechargeable. • Heavier than Leclanché cells. **Uses** • Torches. • Remote controls. • Clocks. • Radios. • Toys.
Primary lithium batteries 	**Advantages** • High energy density. • Light weight. • Very long shelf life. • Very durable. • Compact batteries. **Disadvantages** • Non-rechargeable. • Relatively expensive. **Uses** • Watches. • Cameras. • Calculators. • Heart pacemakers.
Silver-oxide batteries  	**Advantages** • Store large amounts of energy. • Very compact. • Very long operating life. • Very long shelf life. **Disadvantages** • Non-rechargeable. • Very expensive. • Poor low-temperature performance. **Uses** • Hearing aids. • Watches. • Cameras. • Electronic instruments.

Zinc air batteries	Characteristics
Zinc air batteries 	**Advantages** • Relatively cheap. • Available in a wide range of button and coin cell sizes. • Excellent shelf life. • Store large amounts of energy. **Disadvantages** • Sensitive to extreme temperatures. • High internal resistance, producing high internal voltage drops. • Non-rechargeable. **Uses** • Watches. • Hearing aids.

Secondary cells

> **Definition of secondary cell**
>
> A secondary cell is an energy storage device that creates current flow in a circuit by a reversible chemical reaction. Secondary cells can be charged again after discharge.

Secondary cells are 'rechargeable' batteries. This means that the chemical reaction is reversible. After a current has passed through the battery, the active materials return to their original forms.

Table 4.5: Types of secondary cells (batteries)

Type	Characteristics
Rechargeable alkaline batteries	**Advantages** • Relatively cheap. • Easily available. • Require no maintenance. • Retain capacity well. • Have no toxic materials, so they can be easily disposed of. **Disadvantages** • Not suitable for high-drain devices (such as cell phones and portable video games). • High internal resistance. • Limited cycle life. **Uses** • Portable radios. • Remote controls. • Torches. • Clocks.

Nickel-cadmium batteries  	**Advantages** • Low internal resistance. • Available in wide varieties of sizes and capacities. • Good for rapid charge. • Can be stored for long periods of time. **Disadvantages** • Can be easily damaged by overcharging. • Low cell voltage. • Limited recharge life. **Uses** • Toys. • Power tools. • Emergency lighting.
Nickel-metal-hydride batteries  	**Advantages** • Robust batteries. • Low internal resistance. • Work well at different temperatures. • High energy density. • Can be reconditioned. **Disadvantages** • Low cell voltage. • Lower cell capacity and cell voltage than alkaline batteries. • High self-discharge rate. **Uses** • Cell phones. • Cameras. • Medical instruments and equipment.
Lithium-ion batteries  	**Advantages** • High cell voltage. • No liquid, therefore no leaks. • Very high power density. • Light weight. • Very low self-discharge rate. • No reconditioning needed. **Disadvantages** • Relatively high internal resistance. • Very expensive. • Capacity loss when overcharged. **Uses** • Cell phones. • Laptop computers. • Communication equipment. • Cameras.

4.4.2 Choosing a cell or battery

The following factors influence the choice of cells or batteries:

- Primary or secondary.
- Battery capacity.
- Expected usage.
- Cost.
- Size.
- Power and energy requirements.
- Availability.
- Operating temperatures.
- Battery cycle life.
- Internal resistance of cell.

4.4.3 Important terminology

You need to understand the following terminology in order to do simple calculations based on cells and batteries:

- **Cell:** A cell is a source of energy. It stores chemical energy, which it converts into electrical energy as soon as it is connected in a circuit.
- **Battery:** A battery is made up of two or more identical cells. These cells could be connected in series or in parallel.
- **Electromotive force:** This is the voltage measured across the terminals of a battery in an open circuit. It is also called the open-circuit voltage of the battery. (See Figure 4.3.)
- **Potential difference or terminal voltage:** This is the voltage measured across the terminals of a battery in a closed circuit. (See Figure 4.4 and Figure 4.23.)
- **Current:** We use the conventional flow of current.
- **Internal resistance of the battery:** The internal components of the battery have resistance, which we call internal resistance. Internal resistance is denoted by the symbol r and is measured in ohms (Ω). This ***internal resistance*** produces an ***internal voltage drop*** as soon as the circuit is closed or when current begins to flow.

See it online

Cells and batteries
If you have internet access, watch this video:
WCLN – Cells and Batteries – Chemistry by WCLN | https://youtu.be/4oxEn2NHHqE

internal resistance: *the resistance of the internal components of a cell or battery*

internal voltage drop: *decrease in electrical potential caused by the current flowing through the internal components of a battery*

Formula for calculating the internal voltage drop

The internal voltage drop is calculated using the formula:

$$V_{int} = Ir$$

where:

- V_{int} = internal voltage drop in volts (V).
- I = current in amperes (A).
- r = internal resistance in ohms (Ω).

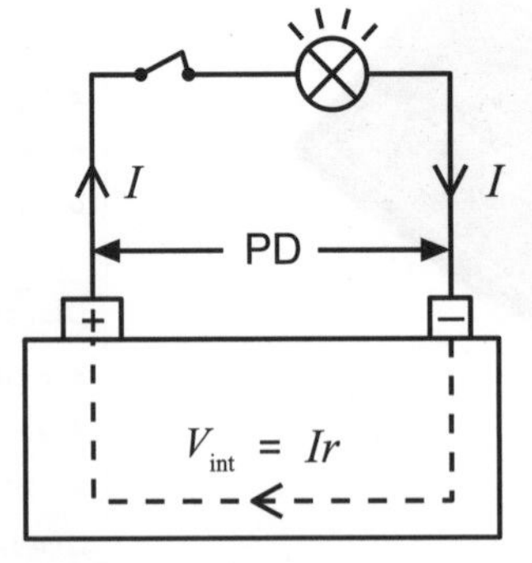

Figure 4.23: Internal voltage drop

Formula for a circuit using a battery as the source of energy

The following formula applies to any circuit using a battery as the source of energy:

emf = PD + internal voltage drop (V_{int})

OR

$E = V + Ir$

$= IR + Ir$ [From Ohm's law: $V = IR$]

$= I(R + r)$

$\therefore I = \frac{E}{R + r}$

where:

- I = current in amperes (A).
- E = emf in volts (V).
- R = external resistance in ohms (Ω).
- r = internal resistance in ohms (Ω).

Important

Note the difference in the following formulae to calculate total current in a circuit:

- $I_{total} = \frac{E_{total}}{R_{total} + r_{total}}$
- $I_{total} = \frac{V_{total}}{R_{total}}$

A battery is made up of two or more identical cells. These cells can be connected either in series or in parallel. Now let us look at how to calculate E_{total} and r_{total}.

4.4.4 Cells connected in series

Figure 4.24 shows a battery with three identical cells connected in series.

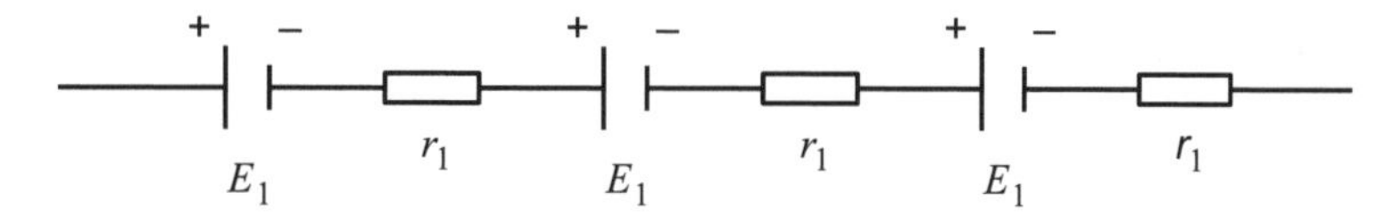

Figure 4.24: Cells in series

Important information for cells in series

- The positive terminal of one cell is connected to the negative terminal of the next cell.
- The internal resistances are also connected in series.
- $E_{total} = E_1 + E_1 + E_1 = 3E_1$
  OR
  $E_{total} = nE_1$
- $r_{total} = r_1 + r_1 + r_1 = 3r_1$
  OR
  $r_{total} = nr_1$

where:

- E_1 = emf of one cell in volts (V).
- r_1 = internal resistance of one cell in ohms (Ω).
- n = number of cells.
- E_{total} = total emf of the battery in volts (V).
- r_{total} = total internal resistance of the battery in ohms (Ω).

Example 4.23

A battery consists of six identical cells in series. Each cell has an emf of 2 V and an internal resistance of 0,1 Ω. This battery supplies power to a bulb with a resistance of 2,4 Ω. Calculate:

1. The total emf of the battery.
2. The total internal resistance of the battery.
3. The total current flowing through the circuit.
4. The internal voltage drop of the battery.
5. The potential difference of the battery.
6. The voltage drop across the bulb.

Solution

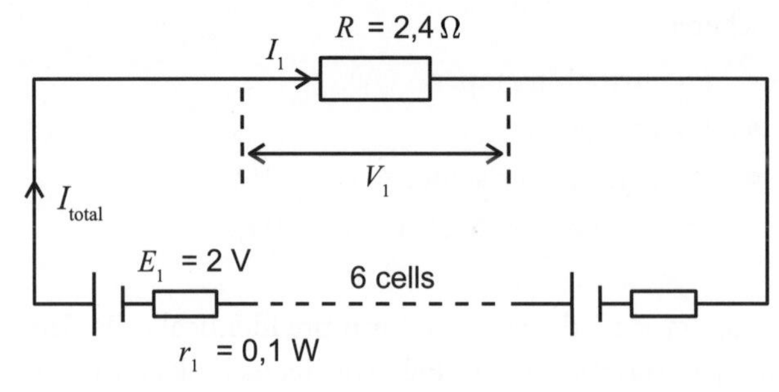

Figure 4.25: Circuit diagram for Example 4.23

1. $E_{total} = nE_1$
   $= (6)(2)$
   $= 12\text{ V}$
2. $r_{total} = nr_1$
   $= (6)(0,1)$
   $= 0,6\ \Omega$
3. $I_{total} = \dfrac{E_{total}}{R_{total} + r_{total}}$
   $= \dfrac{12}{2,4 + 0,6}$
   $= 4\text{ A}$
4. $V_{int} = I_{total} r_{total}$
   $= (4)(0,6)$
   $= 2,4\text{ V}$
5. $V_{total} = I_{total} R_{total}$
   $= (4)(2,4)$
   $= 9,6\text{ V}$
6. $V_1 = I_1 R$
   $= (4)(2,4) \qquad [I_1 = I_{total}]$
   $= 9,6\text{ V}$

4.4.5 Cells connected in parallel

Figure 4.26 shows a battery with three identical cells connected in parallel.

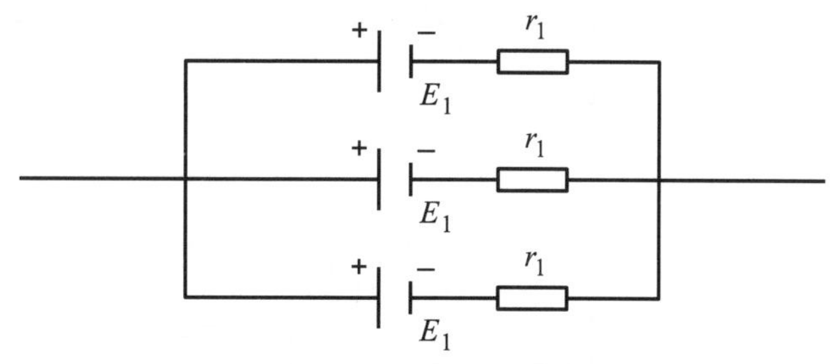

Figure 4.26: Cells in parallel

Important information for cells in parallel

- All positive terminals are connected together and all negative terminals are connected together.
- The internal resistances are also connected in parallel.
- $E_{total} = E_1$, irrespective of the number of cells.
- $$\frac{1}{r_{total}} = \frac{1}{r_1} + \frac{1}{r_1} + \frac{1}{r_1}$$

$$= \frac{1+1+1}{r_1}$$

$$= \frac{3}{r_1}$$

$$\therefore r_{total} = \frac{r_1}{3}$$

or

$$r_{total} = \frac{r_1}{n}$$

where:

- E_{total} = total emf of the battery in volts (V).
- r_{total} = total internal resistance of the battery in ohms (Ω).
- r_1 = internal resistance of one cell in ohms (Ω).
- E_1 = emf of one cell in volts (V).
- n = number of cells.

Example 4.24

A battery has four identical cells connected in parallel. Each cell has an emf of 1,5 V and an internal resistance of 1,1 Ω. The battery is connected across a load with a resistance of 5 Ω. Calculate:

1. The total emf of the battery.
2. The total internal resistance of the battery.
3. The total current flowing through the circuit.
4. The internal voltage drop of the battery.
5. The potential difference of the battery.
6. The voltage drop across the load.

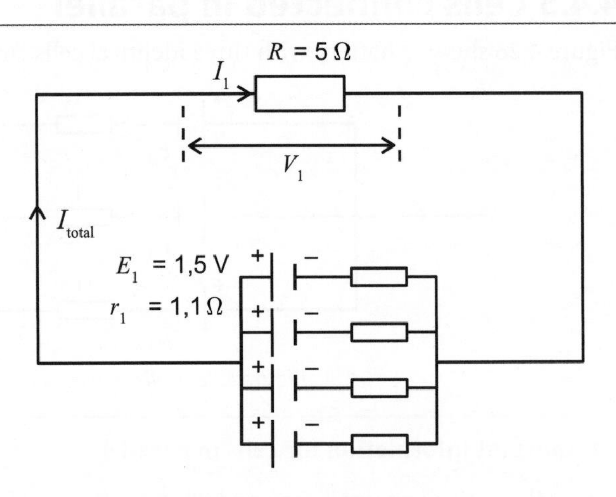

Figure 4.24: Circuit diagram for Example 4.24

Solution

1. $E_{total} = E_1 = 1,5$ V
2. $r_{total} = \frac{r_1}{n}$
   $= \frac{1,1}{4}$
   $= 0,275\ \Omega$
3. $I_{total} = \frac{E_{total}}{R_{total} + r_{total}}$
   $= \frac{1,5}{5 + 0,275}$
   $= 0,284$ A
4. $V_{int} = I_{total} r_{total}$
   $= (0,284)(0,275)$
   $= 0,078$ V
5. $V_{total} = I_{total} R_{total}$
   $= (0,284)(5)$
   $= 1,42$ V
6. $V_1 = I_1 R_1$
   $= (0,284)(5)$ $[I_1 = I_{total}]$
   $= 1,42$ V

Activity 4.7

1. State the function of a cell or battery. (2)
2. Define the following:
   2.1 Primary cell.
   2.2 Secondary cell. (2 × 3 = 6)
3. State the main difference between a primary cell and a secondary cell. (2)
4. What do you understand by internal resistance? (2)
5. What does internal resistance do in a battery? (2)
6. State the formula used to calculate current in a circuit if:
   6.1 The total emf is known.
   6.2 The total potential difference is known. (2 × 1 = 2)
7. A battery has six identical cells. Each cell has an emf of 2 V and an internal resistance of 0,4 Ω. Calculate the total emf and total internal resistance if the cells are connected in:
   7.1 Series. (4)
   7.2 Parallel. (4)
8. Two resistors of 12 Ω and 18 Ω are connected in series. This series combination is supplied by a battery with four identical cells in series. Each cell has an emf of 2,2 V and an internal resistance of 0,4 Ω. Calculate:
   8.1 The total external resistance. (2)
   8.2 The total emf of the battery. (2)
   8.3 The total internal resistance of the battery. (2)
   8.4 The total current in the circuit. (2)
   8.5 The internal voltage drop of the circuit. (2)
   8.6 The potential difference of the battery. (2)
   8.7 The voltage drop across the 12 Ω resistor. (2)
9. Three identical cells are connected in parallel to supply two series-connected loads with resistances of 4 Ω and 5 Ω. Each cell has an emf of 2,1 V and an internal resistance of 1,2 Ω. Calculate:
   9.1 The total emf of the battery. (2)
   9.2 The total internal resistance of the battery. (2)
   9.3 The total external resistance. (2)
   9.4 The total current of the circuit. (2)
   9.5 The internal voltage drop of the battery. (2)
   9.6 The potential difference of the battery. (2)

TOTAL: [50]

Summary of Module 4

We have covered the following in this module. See if you have mastered each of these sections.

Unit 4.1 Basic electricity, Ohm's law and Joule's law

- The movement or flow of negative-charge carriers (electrons) in a specific direction is called current. Current is represented by the symbol I and is measured in amperes (A).
- The flow of electrons from the positive terminal of a battery to the negative terminal is called conventional flow.
- The flow of electrons from the negative terminal to the positive terminal of a battery is called electron flow.
- The flow of electrical current produces the following effects:
  - Lighting.
  - Heating.
  - Chemical.
  - Magnetic.
- The potential difference between two points in a circuit is the work done when one coulomb of charge is moved from one point to the other.
- The unit for potential difference is joules per coulomb or volts.
- Potential difference is simply an electrical pressure that produces current flow in a closed electric circuit.
- An electromotive force is an electrical potential produced by any source of electrical energy. Its function is to initiate and maintain a potential difference.
- The following are sources of electromotive force or sources of electrical energy:
  - Cells or batteries.
  - Generators.
  - Solar energy.
  - Heat.
  - Friction.
- All materials have resistance. Resistance opposes current flow and in this process heat is produced. Resistance is represented by the symbol R and is measured in ohms.
- A conductor is any substance that allows current to flow through it.
- An insulator is any substance that does not allow current to pass through it.
- Resistors are commercially manufactured components and their function is to produce resistance.
- Resistance is needed in an electrical circuit to:
  - Limit current flow.
  - Produce voltage drop.
- Ohm's law states that the current flowing in any closed circuit is directly proportional to the voltage and inversely proportional to the resistance of the circuit. The temperature must remain constant.
- Power is defined as the rate at which work is done or the rate at which energy is consumed.
- Joule's law states that the heat generated in an electrical circuit is proportional to the product of:
  - The square of the current (I^2).
  - The resistance of the circuit (R).
  - The time during which the current flows (t).

Unit 4.2 Methods of connecting resistors in a circuit

- For a circuit with three resistors connected in series:
  - $R_{total} = R_1 + R_2 + R_3$
  - $I_{total} = I_1 = I_2 = I_3$
  - $V_{total} = V_1 + V_2 + V_3$
- For a circuit with three resistors connected in parallel:
  - $\frac{1}{R_{total}} = \frac{1}{R_1} + \frac{1}{R_2} + \frac{1}{R_3}$

  or
  - $R_{total} = \frac{R_1 R_2 R_3}{R_1 R_2 + R_1 R_3 + R_2 R_3}$
  - $I_{total} = I_1 + I_2 + I_3$
  - $V_{total} = V_1 = V_2 = V_3$

Unit 4.3 Factors influencing the resistance of a conductor

- The resistance of any conductor is influenced by the following factors:
  - Length.
  - Cross-sectional area.
  - Resistivity.
  - Temperature.
- Resistivity is the resistance offered by a conductor because of the type of material it is made of. It is a property of materials.
- Resistivity is also called specific resistance and is represented by the symbol ρ (rho). It is measured in ohm metres.
- The temperature coefficient of resistance is defined as the increase or decrease in resistance per ohm original resistance per degree rise in temperature and is represented by the symbol α (alpha).
- Conductors such as silver, copper and aluminium experience an increase in resistance with an increase in temperature and have a positive temperature coefficient of resistance.
- Carbon, electrolytes, semiconductors (silicon and germanium) and insulators experience a decrease in resistance with an increase in temperature and have a negative temperature coefficient of resistance.
- Alloys such as manganin and nichrome experience little change in resistance with an increase in temperature, which makes them suitable for the manufacture of resistors.

Unit 4.4 Cells and batteries

- A battery is made up of two or more identical cells, connected either in series or in parallel.
- The function of cells or batteries is to store chemical energy which will be converted into electrical energy once the cells or batteries are connected in an electrical circuit.
- Primary cells are non-rechargeable. The chemical reaction is irreversible and the cells cannot convert electrical energy back into chemical energy.
- Secondary cells are rechargeable batteries, so the chemical reaction is reversible. After a current has passed through the battery, the active materials return to their original forms.
- Electromotive force is the voltage measured across the terminals of a battery of an open circuit. It is also called the open-circuit voltage of the battery.
- Potential difference or terminal voltage is the voltage measured across the terminals of a battery in a closed circuit.
- Batteries have internal resistance which will produce an internal voltage drop when current begins to flow through the circuit.
- For cells connected in series:
  - $E_{total} = nE_1$
  - $r_{total} = nr_1$
- For cells connected in parallel:
  - $E_{total} = E_1$
  - $r_{total} = \frac{r_1}{n}$

Summative assessment for Module 4

1. Why can valence electrons in certain materials easily detach themselves from the parent atom? (3)
2. What do you understand by the following?
   2.1 Conventional flow of current. (2)
   2.2 Electron flow. (2)
3. Complete the following statements by filling in the blanks.
   3.1 ___________ is required to produce current flow in a closed electrical circuit.
   3.2 ___________ is required to initiate and maintain a potential difference.
   3.3 ___________ opposes current flow in an electric circuit and in the process of resisting current flow _________ is produced. (4 × 1 = 4)
4. What are resistors and what is their main function? (2)
5. State three examples of good conductors. (3)
6. What does 'incandescent' mean? (2)
7. State the three formulae that are given by the Ohm's law triangle. (3)
8. A stove plate draws 6,25 A of current from a 240 V supply. Calculate the resistance of the stove plate. (3)
9. An oven element with a resistance of 22,5 Ω is supplied by a 240 V energy source. Calculate the current drawn by the element. (3)
10. A wall-mounted heater draws 10 A of current from the supply. If the resistance of the heating element is 23 Ω, calculate the potential difference of the supply. (3)
11. State three formulae used to calculate electrical power. (3)
12. What is a resistive circuit? (1)
13. Convert:
    13.1 42,7 minutes to seconds. (1)
    13.2 8,5 hours to seconds. (1)
    13.3 3 475 208 J to MJ. (1)
    13.4 988 026 J to kJ. (1)
14. An incandescent lamp has a resistance of 576 Ω. If the lamp is supplied by 230 V, calculate:
    14.1 The current drawn by the lamp. (3)
    14.2 The power rating of the lamp. (3)
    14.3 The energy dissipated by the lamp in 90 minutes. (3)
15. A bread toaster is rated at 850 W and it operates at 220 V. Calculate:
    15.1 The current drawn from the supply. (3)
    15.2 The energy dissipated by the toaster in 2,2 minutes. (3)
    15.3 The resistance of the heating element. (3)
16. What do you understand by voltage drop? (2)

17. Two resistors are connected in series. The voltage drop across these resistors is 120 V and 80 V. If the total power drawn from the supply is 1 100 W, calculate:
    17.1 The potential difference of the supply. (3)
    17.2 The current drawn from the supply. (3)
    17.3 The current flow through each resistor. (3)
    17.4 The energy dissipated by the circuit in 1,25 hours. Give your answer in MJ. (3)
18. Three resistors of 18 Ω, 24 Ω and 36 Ω are connected in parallel across a 100 V supply. Calculate:
    18.1 The total resistance of the circuit. (3)
    18.2 The total current flow through the circuit. (3)
    18.3 The voltage drop across each resistor. (2)
    18.4 The current flow through each resistor. (6)
    18.5 The power drawn by each resistor. (6)
19. Three resistors are connected in parallel. The first two resistors are 20 Ω and 30 Ω and the third resistor is unknown. If the total resistance of the circuit is 6 Ω, calculate the resistance of the unknown resistor. (4)
20. Two resistors of 10 Ω and 20 Ω are connected in parallel. This parallel combination is then connected in series with another parallel combination with a 30 Ω resistor and a 40 Ω resistor. The circuit is connected to a 100 V supply. Calculate:
    20.1 The total resistance of the circuit. (5)
    20.2 The total current drawn from the supply. (3)
    20.3 The voltage drop across each parallel branch. (4)
    20.4 The current flow through each resistor. (8)
    20.5 The power drawn by the 40 Ω resistor. (3)
    20.6 The energy dissipated by the 10 Ω resistor in 2 minutes. (3)
21. State whether each of the following is true or false. If false, give a reason.
    21.1 The resistance of a conductor is inversely proportional to its length. (2)
    21.2 The resistance of a conductor is directly proportional to its cross-sectional area. (2)
22. State two formulae that are used to calculate the cross-sectional area of a round conductor. (2)
23. A copper conductor has a length of 0,65 km and a cross-sectional area of 1 mm^2. Calculate the resistance of the conductor if the resistivity of copper is 0,017 μΩ m. (4)
24. Calculate the diameter of an aluminium conductor with a length of 1 275 m and a resistance of 1,8 Ω. Take the resistivity of aluminium to be 0,027 μΩ m. (5)
25. Explain what is meant by a negative temperature coefficient of resistance. (3)
26. The primary winding of a transformer has a resistance of 4,7 Ω at 0 °C. Determine the resistance of the winding at a temperature of 65 °C. The temperature coefficient of resistance is 0,0051/°C at 0 °C. (4)
27. Determine the temperature at which the resistance of the field coils of a generator will be 25 Ω. The resistance of these coils at 0 °C is 18 Ω. Take the temperature coefficient of resistance to be 0,0044/°C at 0 °C. (4)

28. A battery consists of six identical cells. Each cell has an emf of 1,85 V and an internal resistance of 1 Ω. Determine the total emf and internal resistance of the battery if the cells are connected in:

28.1 Series. (4)

28.2 Parallel. (4)

29. A battery with a total emf of 12 V and an internal resistance of 3 Ω is used to supply a load with a resistance of 4 Ω. Calculate:

29.1 The current drawn from the supply. (3)

29.2 The potential difference of the battery. (3)

29.3 The voltage drop across the load. (3)

30. A battery supplies an appliance that draws 3 A of current. If the battery has an emf of 18 V and an internal resistance of 2,2 Ω, calculate:

30.1 The resistance of the appliance. (4)

30.2 The voltage drop across the appliance. (3)

TOTAL: [170]

Conductors and insulating materials

Module

5

Overview of Module 5

In any electrical system, the load is connected to the supply by using conductors. These conductors are electrically separated from one another by using insulators.

In this module we are going to learn about the characteristics of conductors, insulators and semi-conductors and look at examples of each.

When you have completed this module, you should be able to:

Unit 5.1: Conductors, insulators and semiconductors

- State what is meant by a conductor.
- State the characteristics and examples of materials that are good conductors.
- State what is meant by an insulator.
- State the characteristic of good insulators.
- Provide examples of good insulators.
- State what is meant by semi-conductors.
- State the two most commonly used semi-conductors.

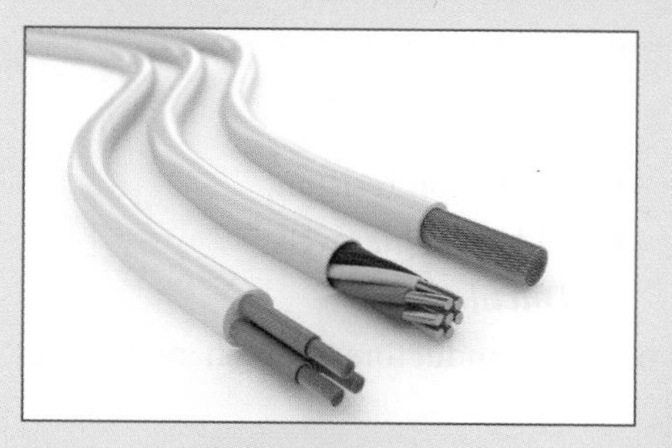

Figure 5.1: A cable is made up of separately insulated conductors

Starter activity

Discuss the following in class:

- Gold is an excellent conductor of electricity. Why do you think that the use of gold as a conductor is very limited?
- Copper is a reasonably expensive metal, which is why it is targeted by cable thieves. In spite of this, copper is still the most popular conductor in the electrical industry. Why do you think this is so?
- Silicone is an excellent insulator. Do you know what silicone looks like and feels like?

Unit 5.1: Conductors, insulators and semiconductors

You learned in Module 4 that materials that are used in the electrical industry can be classified as conductors, insulators or semiconductors.

5.1.1 Conductors

Definition of a conductor

An electrical conductor is any substance that allows electrons to move easily from one atom to another when a potential difference is applied across this substance. This means that a conductor is any material that is capable of conducting electric current.

Conductors are classified as good or bad conductors depending on their ***conductivity***.

Good conductors (materials with a high conductivity) are used in the transmission and distribution of electrical energy and also in the manufacture of electrical machines and equipment.

There are many materials available and there are many factors to be considered before selecting the appropriate conductor for a particular application.

The chosen material must be:

- Affordable.
- Readily available.
- Highly conductive.
- Mechanically strong.
- Flexible.
- Corrosion resistant.
- Able to ***solder*** well.
- ***Ductile.***

We will look at the following examples of good conductors, their characteristics and applications:

- Silver.
- Copper.
- Gold.
- Aluminium.

We will also look at the characteristics and applications of carbon. Carbon is not a good conductor, but it has certain valuable properties that make it very useful in the electrical industry.

Silver

Silver is the best known conductor of electricity, but its use is very limited because it is very expensive. Silver is very ductile and ***malleable***.

Silver is used in batteries and ***light-emitting diode (LED)*** chips. Silver tungsten alloys are used as contacts in circuit breakers, relays and contactors.

conductivity: *a property or characteristic that describes how well a material allows current to flow through it*

solder: *join to another substance using a filler substance with a lower melting point (called solder)*

ductile: *can be drawn out into a thin wire*

malleable: *can be hammered or pressed into shape without breaking or cracking*

light-emitting diode (LED): *a semiconductor light source that emits light when a current flows through it*

Copper

Copper is the most commonly used conductor in the electrical industry. Copper has a very high conductivity, is malleable, is ductile, solders easily and has a high melting point.

Copper can be used in different forms for different applications. This is why it is very popular in the electrical industry.

Table 5.1: Uses for different types of copper

Type	Description	Use
Hard-drawn copper	More rigid, produces greater hardness and strength.	Used to manufacture wire for panel wiring, commutator segments and special cases of overhead lines.
Annealed copper	Copper that has undergone a heat treatment process. This process changes the physical properties of the material. The copper is softened, making it more flexible and increasing its conductivity.	Used to manufacture water pipes. Also used for house wiring and to manufacture cables.
Stranded conductors	Conductors are stranded to make them more flexible. This also makes it easy to coil conductors and cables. Stranded conductors are formed by twisting many thin strands together in layers.	Used for house wiring and to manufacture cables.

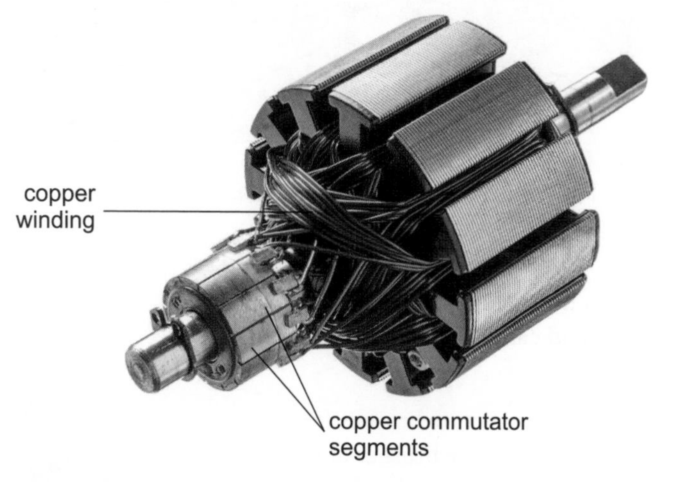

Figure 5.2: Copper used in the rotating part of a DC machine

Gold

Gold has a very high conductivity, is very malleable and is also very ductile. Gold is a precious metal and is therefore very expensive, which limits its use.

Because of its excellent mechanical properties, gold is used in many electronic devices such as cell phones, television sets, GPS units, desktop computers and laptops.

Aluminium

Aluminium is the second most popular conductor used in the electrical industry, after copper.

Table 5.2: Advantages and disadvantages of aluminium

Advantages	Disadvantages
• Highly conductive. • Lightweight. • Relatively cheap. • Readily available. • Fairly resistant to corrosion.	• Low ***tensile strength***. • Does not solder and weld easily.

tensile strength: *ability of a material to withstand being stretch or pulled without breaking*

Aluminium is used:

- To manufacture cables.
- Commonly as an overhead conductor (transmission lines) because of its light weight. A challenge is that aluminium has a low tensile strength. To overcome this challenge, the electrical industry uses steel-cored stranded aluminium conductors.

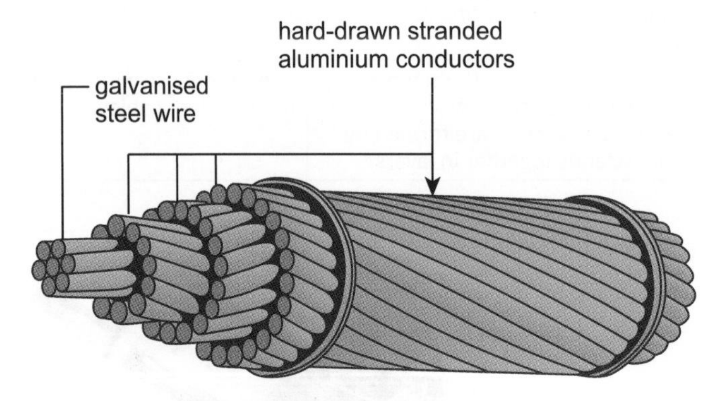

Figure 5.3: Steel-covered stranded aluminium conductors

Carbon

Carbon does not have a high conductivity, but it is hard-wearing and can withstand extremely high temperatures.

Carbon is used to manufacture brushes for motors and generators. These brushes are used to make an electrical connection between a stationary circuit and a rotating machine part. At the point of contact with the rotating machine part, a large amount of heat is produced because of friction.

Carbon dust acts as a lubricant.

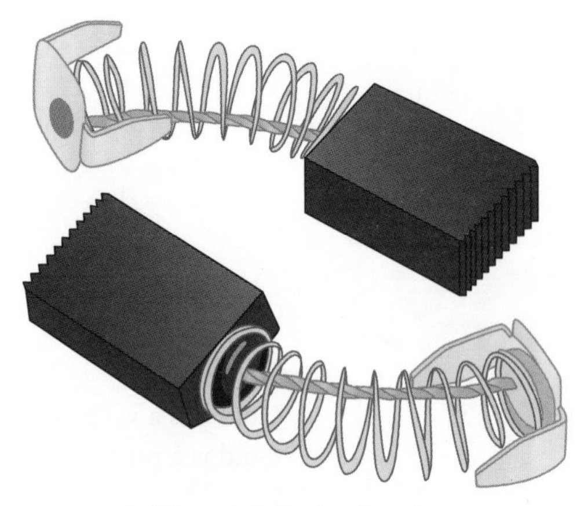

Figure 5.4: Carbon brushes

Activity 5.1

1. Materials that are used in the electrical industry fall in three categories. List these categories. (3)
2. What is a conductor? (2)
3. State five factors that influence the choice of a good conductor for a particular application. (5)
4. Name the best known conductor. (1)
5. Why is the use of the conductor mentioned in Question 4 limited? (1)
6. State three uses of silver in the electrical industry. (3)
7. State two uses of hard-drawn copper. (2)
8. What is the purpose of stranding conductors? (2)
9. Why is the use of gold as a conductor very limited? (1)
10. State two uses of aluminium as a conductor. (2)
11. State the main reason for using aluminium as overhead transmission line conductors. (1)
12. State two reasons why carbon is used to manufacture brushes. (2)

TOTAL: [25]

5.1.2 Insulators

Definition of an insulator

An electrical insulator is any substance that does not allow electrons to move easily from one atom to another when a potential difference is applied across this substance. This means that an insulator is any material that does not conduct electric current.

Insulators are used to electrically separate conductors, and sometimes to support them.

Good insulators have an extremely high resistance and will therefore oppose the flow of current.

The choice of an insulator for a particular application will depend on whether the insulator is:

- Flexible.
- Robust.
- Heat resistant.
- Waterproof.
- Suitable for high-voltage use.

We will look at the following good insulators and their characteristics and uses:

- Porcelain.
- Glass.
- Mica.
- Asbestos.
- Silicone.
- Bakelite.
- Polyvinyl chloride (PVC).
- Vulcanised rubber.
- Polycarbonate compounds.

Porcelain

Porcelain is used extensively in overhead line insulators. These insulators have a high ***dielectric strength*** and can withstand high-voltage stresses. They can also withstand the high temperatures caused by ***flashovers*** in overhead transmission lines.

Porcelain is porous and any water or moisture entering the material will reduce its insulating properties, so it is waterproofed by ***glazing***. Glazing allows any dust or dirt to slide off easily.

dielectric strength: *insulating strength*

flashover: *arcing (sparking) across insulators caused by overvoltage on transmission lines*

glazing: *adding a layer of glass to porcelain using very high temperatures*

annealed: *heat treated to increase ductility and reduce hardness*

coefficient of thermal expansion: *describes the fractional change in the size of an object when its temperature changes*

Glass

Annealed tough glass is fast replacing porcelain insulators as overhead line insulators. This is because glass:

- Is cheaper.
- Is naturally waterproof.
- Has a higher dielectric strength.
- Has a higher tensile strength.
- Does not heat up in the sun as porcelain does.
- Has a low ***coefficient of thermal expansion***.

Figure 5.5: Glass overhead line insulator

Mica

Mica is a silicate mineral found in granite and other rocks. It is an extremely tough material that can withstand very high temperatures of up to 1 000 °C.

Mica is used to support heating elements of bread toasters. It is also used as insulation between commutator segments of DC machines.

Asbestos

hygroscopic: *tending to absorb moisture from the environment*

resin: *synthetic organic polymer used as the basis of plastics, adhesives, varnishes, or other products*

bakelite: *a type of synthetic resin*

polymer: *chemical compound with molecules bonded together in long, repeating chains*

Asbestos is a good insulator that can withstand very high temperatures. Because of its robust nature, it is used to support heating elements. It is also used as insulation for the internal wiring of stoves.

The major disadvantage of asbestos is that it is ***hygroscopic***. This means that it absorbs water easily. To overcome this challenge, asbestos has to be filled with a waterproof ***resin***.

Silicone

Silicone looks and feels like rubber. It should not be confused with silicon, the element, which is one of its components. Silicone can serve as an effective insulator within a temperature range of –100 °C to 300 °C. It has many useful properties, such as:

- Flexibility.
- Fire resistance.
- Good dielectric strength at high voltages.
- Good thermal conductivity.
- Good tensile strength.

Silicone is used to insulate conductors for high-temperature applications. It is also used for high-voltage insulation and to manufacture insulating tapes.

Bakelite

Bakelite has excellent insulating properties. It is robust and heat- and chemical resistant. It can easily be moulded to form casings for various electrical devices. Bakelite is light and durable, non-flammable, and can retain its shape.

It is used to manufacture circuit-breaker casings, telephone casings and vehicle distributor caps.

Figure 5.6: PVC insulating tape

Polyvinyl chloride (PVC)

PVC is a plastic ***polymer*** used extensively in the electrical industry. It is waterproof, but not heat resistant. PVC is tough, flexible, relatively cheap and easy to colour.

Table 5.3: Forms and uses of PVC

Form	Use
Rigid form	• Manufacture of pipes. • As supports for non-heating objects.
Flexible form	• Insulation in electrical cables. • Manufacture of insulating tapes and inflatable objects.

Vulcanised rubber

Vulcanising is a chemical process by which the physical properties of natural rubber are improved. Natural rubber is very sticky, deforms easily when heated and becomes brittle when cold.

vulcanising: *hardening by treating with sulphur at a high temperature*

tinned: *copper conductors are coated with a thin layer of tin to reduce oxidation and increase their lifespan*

By a chemical process, sulphur is added to rubber. The final product has a higher tensile strength and becomes more elastic. The disadvantage is that sulphur reacts with copper. To prevent this reaction, copper must be ***tinned***.

Vulcanised rubber is used to insulate low- to medium-voltage flexible cables.

Polycarbonate compounds

Polycarbonate is a durable material that has a high impact resistance and is also scratch resistant. Some grades of polycarbonates are transparent. These materials are naturally waterproof.

Polycarbonate compounds are used in safety glasses, vehicle headlamp lenses, eyeglass lenses, CDs and DVDs.

Activity 5.2

1. State the function of insulators. (2)
2. State five advantages of annealed glass compared to porcelain. (5)
3. State one use of porcelain as an insulator. (1)
4. State one disadvantage of porcelain as an insulator. (1)
5. State how the disadvantage mentioned in Question 4 is overcome. (1)
6. State two functions of mica as an insulator. (2)
7. State two important characteristics of mica as an insulator. (2)
8. State two characteristics of asbestos as an insulator. (2)
9. State one major disadvantage of asbestos. (1)
10. State how the disadvantage mentioned in Question 9 is overcome. (1)
11. State five properties of Bakelite as an insulator. (5)
12. State three characteristics of PVC as an insulator. (3)
13. What do you understand by vulcanising? (3)
14. State three characteristics of polycarbonate compounds. (3)
15. State three uses of polycarbonate compounds. (3)

TOTAL: [35]

5.2.3 Semiconductors

Definition of a semiconductor

A semiconductor is a substance that has properties of electrical conductivity falling between those of a conductor and those of an insulator.

diode: *a two-terminal semiconductor device that allows current to flow in one direction only*

transistor: *a semiconductor device that regulates current flow and acts as an amplifier or a switch*

Silicon and germanium

Materials such as germanium and silicon are known as semiconductors, because they have conducting properties that lie between those of conductors and those of insulators.

We use these semiconductor materials to produce solid-state components such as ***diodes*** and ***transistors***.

Activity 5.3

1.	What are semiconductors?	(1)
2.	Name two semiconductor materials.	(2)
3.	Name two uses of semiconductor materials.	(2)
		TOTAL: [5]

Summary of Module 5

We have covered the following in this module. See if you have mastered each of these sections.

Unit 5.1 Conductors, insulators and semiconductors

- Materials that are used in the electrical industry can be classified as conductors, insulators or semiconductors.
- A conductor is any material that is capable of conducting electric current.
- Materials with a high conductivity are used in the transmission and distribution of electrical energy and in the manufacture of electrical machines and equipment.
- Silver is the best known conductor of electricity.
- Copper is the most commonly used conductor in the electrical industry. Copper conductors are stranded in order to make them more flexible and to make it easy to coil conductors and cables.
- Gold has a very high conductivity, is very malleable and is also very ductile.
- Aluminium is the second most popular conductor used in the electrical industry.
- Carbon does not have a high conductivity but is hard-wearing and is capable of withstanding extremely high temperatures.
- Insulators are used to electrically separate conductors and sometimes to support them.
- Porcelain is used extensively in overhead line insulators. These insulators have a high dielectric strength and can withstand high-voltage stresses.
- Annealed tough glass is fast replacing porcelain insulators as overhead line insulators.
- Mica is an extremely tough material that can withstand very high temperatures of up to 1 000 °C.
- Asbestos is a good insulator that can withstand very high temperatures. Because of its robust nature, it is used to support heating elements.

- Silicone looks and feels like rubber. It serves as an effective insulator within a temperature range of −100 °C to 300 °C.
- Bakelite has excellent insulating properties.
- PVC is a plastic polymer used extensively in the electrical industry. It is waterproof, but not heat resistant.
- Vulcanising is a chemical process by which the physical properties of natural rubber is improved.
- Polycarbonate is a durable material that has a high impact resistance and is also scratch resistant.
- Materials such as germanium and silicon are known as semiconductors, because they have conducting properties that lie between those of a conductor and those of an insulator.
- Semiconductor materials are used to produce solid-state components such as diodes and transistors.

Summative assessment for Module 5

1. What do you understand by conductivity? (3)
2. State five conductors used in the electrical industry. (5)
3. What do you understand by the following?
   - 3.1 Ductile. (2)
   - 3.2 Malleable. (3)
   - 3.3 Annealed copper. (2)
4. State three characteristics of gold as a conductor. (3)
5. State five characteristics of aluminium as a conductor. (5)
6. State five factors to be considered when choosing an insulator for a particular application. (5)
7. State three important characteristics of porcelain as an insulator. (3)
8. State two reasons for glazing porcelain insulators. (2)
9. State two functions of asbestos as an insulator. (2)
10. State five characteristics of silicone as an insulator. (5)
11. State three uses of Bakelite. (3)
12. State two forms in which PVC is used. (2)

TOTAL: [45]

Wiring of premises

Module

6

Overview of Module 6

Every aspect concerning the wiring of premises, whether industrial or domestic, has to conform to the regulations as laid down in the Wiring Code SANS 10142-1: 2020 and its subsequent amendments.

In this module we are going to learn about the wiring on domestic electrical installations and the protective devices used in electrical installations.

When you have completed this module, you should be able to:

Unit 6.1: Wiring domestic electrical installations

- Identify and draw different types of International Electrotechnical Commission (IEC) symbols to be used in domestic electrical installations.
- State the size of conductors and protective devices that are commonly used in the subcircuits of electrical installations.
- Draw labelled circuit diagrams for the following subcircuits of a single-phase domestic installation.
  - Light circuit (one-way, two-way and intermediate switching).
  - Socket-outlet circuit (maximum two outlets).
  - Geyser circuit.
  - Stove circuit.
  - Distribution board.
  - Single-phase supply to installation (overhead and underground).
- Apply the SANS 10142-1 to all learning outcomes.

Unit 6.2: Protective devices for electrical installations

- State the function of the following protective devices:
  - Earth leakage relay, circuit breaker, fuse, lighting arrestor.

*Figure 6.1: **Conduit box** and circuit breakers on a wiring diagram*

conduit box: *round PVC box with a lid in which conductor joints are made*

Starter activity

Discuss the following in class:

- You switch on the lights of a staircase on the ground floor and you climb to the second floor where you then switch off the lights. Try to draw a diagram of this lighting circuit.
- Geysers are normally situated above the ceiling in our homes. How is it possible to work safely on the geyser without the danger of somebody accidentally switching on the circuit breaker located in the distribution board?

Note | SANS 10142-1

- The regulations quoted in this book are extracts from:
  - SANS 10142-1: 2020 | The wiring of premises Part 1: Low-voltage installations.
- These regulations are updated regularly – please read them together with any subsequent amendments.

Unit 6.1: Wiring domestic electrical installations

Domestic wiring is a process of installing and connecting cables (conductors) and related devices to safely distribute energy from the supplier to equipment and appliances in the home. It involves the proper installation of switches, distribution boards, socket outlets and different electric ***subcircuits***.

subcircuit: *a distinct circuit of an electrical installation*

6.1.1 Wiring diagrams and IEC symbols

Definition of wiring diagram

A wiring diagram is a line drawing showing how the electrical wiring and components of an electrical installation should be connected.

All electrical drawings or wiring diagrams use graphic symbols to represent electrical components. In South Africa we use the standard symbols published by the International Electrotechnical Commission (IEC).

The functions of these symbols are to assist with the following:

- Consistent interpretation of wiring diagrams.
- Drawing up a materials list for a job.
- Uniform drawings.
- Fault finding.

Table 6.1 shows some of the standard IEC electrical wiring symbols.

Table 6.1: Standard IEC electrical wiring symbols

Symbol	Description	Symbol	Description
	Cell		***Capacitor***
	Battery		***Polarised capacitor***
	AC generator		***Variable capacitor***
	DC generator		Coil
	Motor		Resistor
	Voltmeter		Variable resistor
	Ammeter		Conductors cross
	Ohmmeter		Conductors join
	Galvanometer		Neutral conductor
	Earth connection		***Double-wound transformer***
	Frame connection		***Current transformer***
	Fuse		Single-pole switch
	Circuit breaker		Two-way switch
	Disconnector		Intermediate switch
	Switch disconnector		Push-button switch
	Bell		

capacitor: *an electronic device that stores electrical energy in an electric field*

polarised capacitor: *a capacitor with an anode (+) and a cathode (–)*

variable capacitor: *a capacitor whose capacitance can be varied*

voltmeter: *an instrument used for measuring electrical potential difference between two points in an electric circuit in volts (V)*

ammeter: *an instrument for measuring electric current in amperes (A)*

ohmmeter: *an instrument used for measuring electrical resistances in ohms (Ω)*

galvanometer: *a sensitive moving-coil analogue instrument used to detect and measure very small quantities of electric current*

double-wound transformer: *transformer having two windings which are electrically isolated from each other.*

frame connection: *term used in structural steel engineering showing a simple connection made to a steel member*

current transformer: *instrument transformer used to step down currents to values that are safe to measure*

switch disconnector: *an on-load isolator used to make, carry and break current flow under normal circuit conditions*

6.1.2 Parts of a domestic electrical installation

In this unit we will consider the wiring of ***single-phase*** domestic installations.

single-phase: *a supply (system) having only one live conductor*

Figure 6.2 shows the sections of a domestic electrical installation.

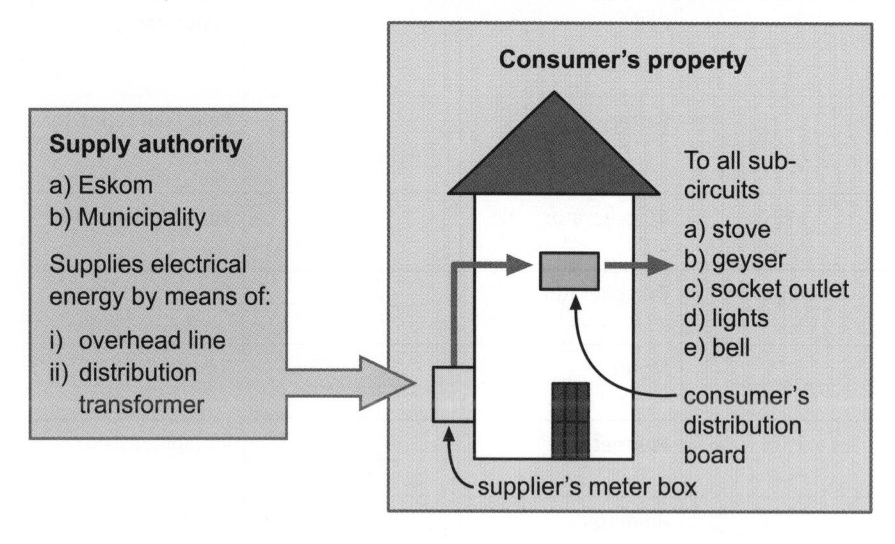

Figure 6.2: Sections of an electrical installation

6.1.3 Single-phase supply to an installation

The supply authority supplies electrical energy to an electrical installation using one of the following methods of connection:

- Aerial conductors connected to an overhead ***transmission line*** (Figure 6.3).
- An underground cable connected to an overhead transmission line (Figure 6.4).
- An underground cable connected to a ***distribution transformer***.

transmission line: *an overhead system of conductors that transfers electrical power from generating plants to the substations that deliver power to customers*

distribution transformer: *transformer that ensures the final reduction (step down) of voltage before supplying consumers*

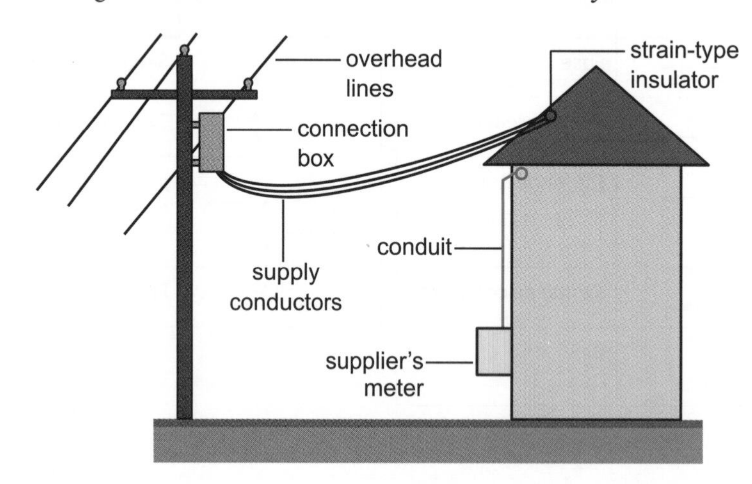

Figure 6.3: Electrical energy taken off an overhead transmission line using aerial conductors

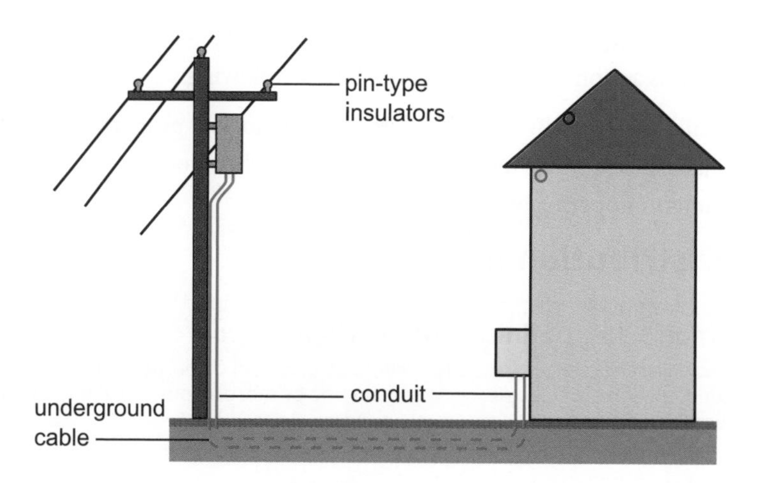

Figure 6.4: Electrical energy taken off an overhead transmission line using an underground cable

Supplier's meter box

meter (electrical): *device that measures the amount of electrical energy consumed by a residence or business*

In most cases, the supplier's meter box is mounted outside the house on the wall closest to the point of electrical entry. Figure 6.5 shows the internal wiring of a supplier's meter box.

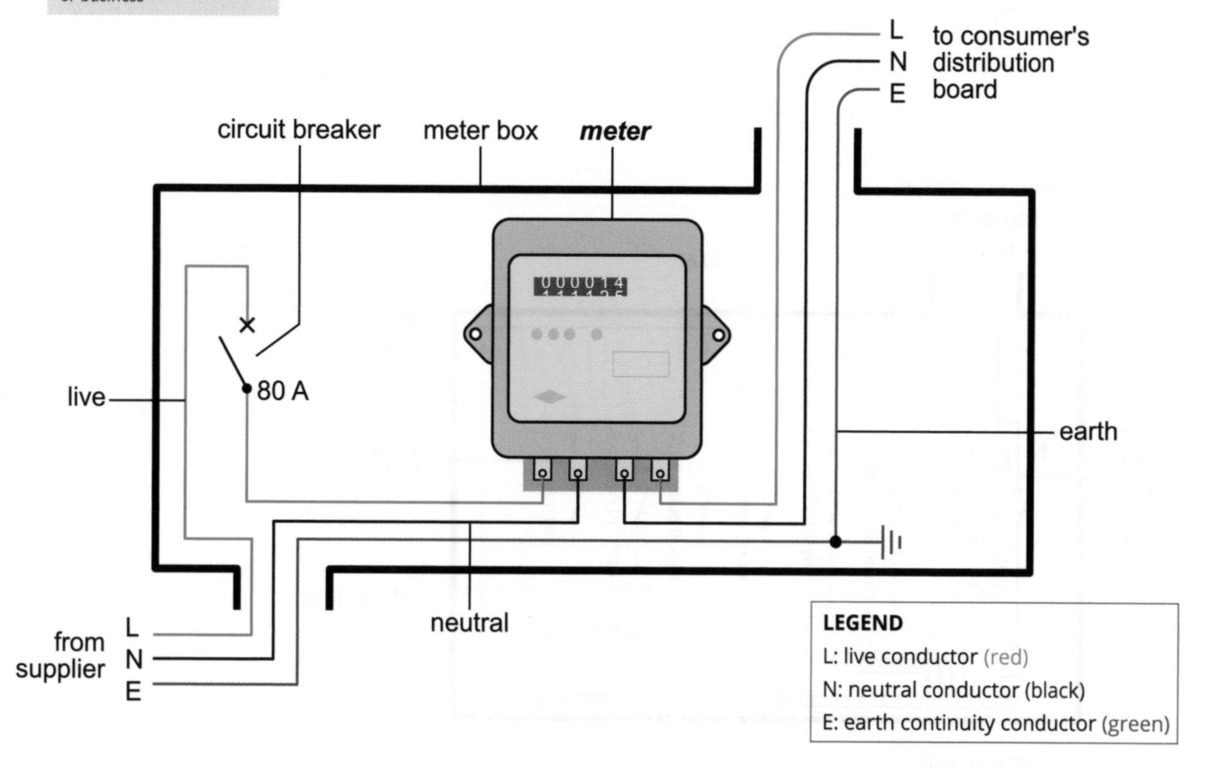

Figure 6.5: Internal wiring of supplier's meter box

Some municipalities are relocating these energy meters into electrical kiosks (boxes) found outside the consumer's property. There are many meters in each kiosk, recording the units of electricity consumed by the consumers living in that street. This action was brought about by the following:

- The challenges faced by meter readers to access locked properties.
- The challenges faced by meter readers with regard to dogs.
- Consumers tampering with meters.

6.1.4 Distribution boards

Regulation 3.25 | Definition of distribution board

A distribution board is an enclosure that contains electrical equipment for the distribution or control of electrical power from one or more incoming circuits to one or more outgoing circuits.

Important

Please note that every subcircuit of the installation starts at the distribution board and that every subcircuit will have the following:

- A ***live conductor*** (red) connected to the load side of the relevant circuit breaker.
- A ***neutral conductor*** (black) connected to the relevant ***neutral bar***. In Figure 6.6b, only the plug circuits are protected by the earth leakage relay and therefore only the neutrals of the plug circuits will be connected to neutral bar 2.
- An ***earth continuity conductor*** connected to the ***earth bar***.

live conductor: *conductor carrying current from the point of supply to the point of consumption*

neutral conductor: *conductor returning current from the point of consumption to the point of supply*

neutral bar: *copper bar in the distribution board to which all neutral conductors are connected*

earth continuity conductor: *conductor, including any clamp or terminal, that connects the consumer's earth terminal (earth bar) to the exposed conductive parts of an installation*

earth bar: *copper bar in the distribution board to which all earth continuity conductors and the earth lead are connected*

Figure 6.6a shows the internal wiring of a distribution board where the earth leakage relay (ELR) is used as the main-switch disconnector.

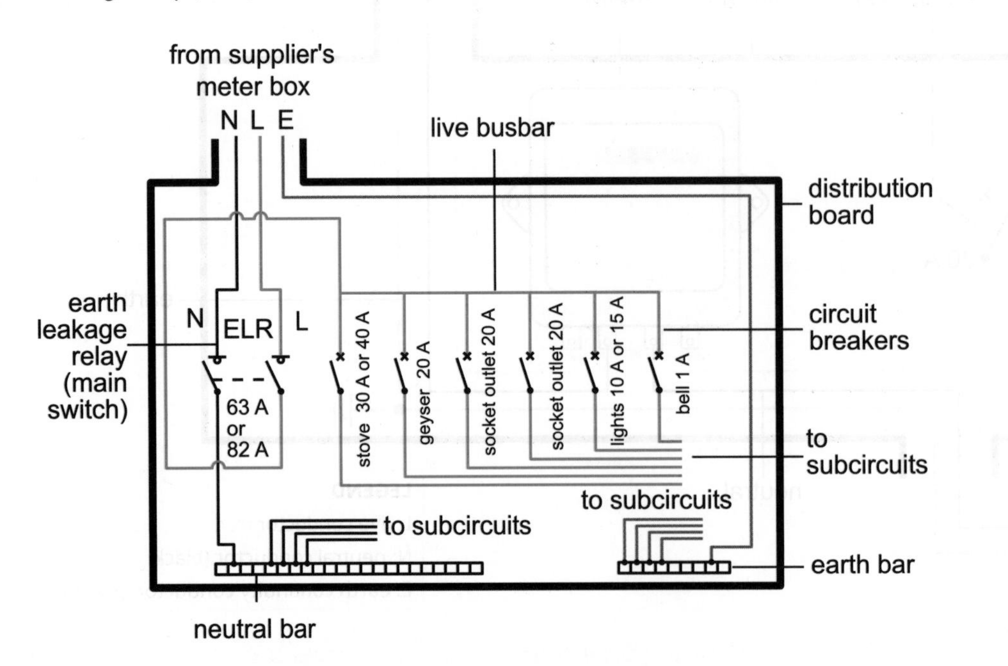

Figure 6.6a: Distribution board (ELR used as main-switch disconnector)

In Figure 6.6b, the earth leakage relay is not used as the main-switch disconnector.

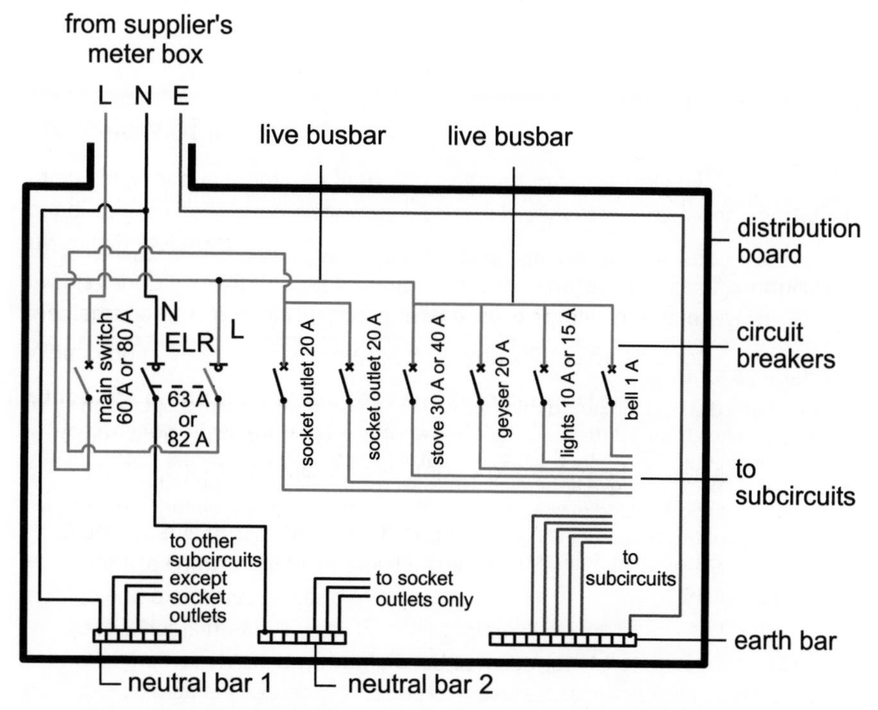

Figure 6.6b: Distribution board (ELR not used as main-switch disconnector)

Table 6.2 shows the basic components included in a normal domestic distribution board.

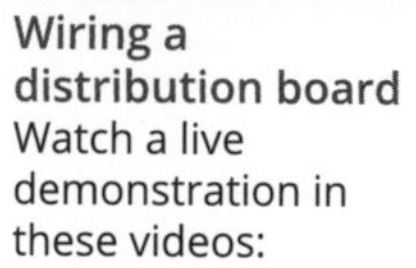

See it online

Wiring a distribution board
Watch a live demonstration in these videos:

- How to Wire a Distribution Board by Jean B | https://youtu.be/fFBFJ97C3DI
- How to wire a distribution board and load circuits – tutorial by ecological time | https://youtu.be/6O90pFfHuOo

Table 6.2: Basic components of a distribution board

Subcircuit	Component	Size	Conductor size
	Main switch	60 A or 80 A	10 mm^2 or 16 mm^2
	Earth leakage	63 A or 82 A	10 mm^2 or 16 mm^2
Stove (cooking appliance)	Circuit breaker	30 A or 40 A	4 mm^2 or 6 mm^2
Geyser	Circuit breaker	20 A	2,5 mm^2
Socket outlet	Circuit breaker	20 A	2,5 mm^2
Lights	Circuit breaker	10 A or 15 A	1,5 mm^2
Bell	Circuit breaker	1 A	1 mm^2
Internal wiring of a distribution board is done with 10 mm^2 conductors.			

The following are some relevant regulations from SANS 10142-1 concerning distribution boards.

Regulation 6.6 | Distribution boards

Regulation 6.6.1.1

Each distribution board shall be controlled by a switch disconnector. The switch disconnector shall

a) be mounted in the distribution board or adjacent to the distribution board in the same room,

b) in the case of the main or first distribution board of an installation, be labelled as 'main switch',

c) have a danger notice on or near it. The danger notice shall give instructions that the switch disconnector be switched off in the event of ***inadvertent*** contact or leakage.

Regulation 6.6.1.6

Any point of a distribution board that has to be reached during normal operation shall not exceed a height of 2,2 m above floor (or walking) level. However, the board may be mounted higher if it can be disconnected from the supply by a switch disconnector that is less than 2,2 m above floor level. Unless a residential distribution board is housed in an enclosure and direct access cannot be obtained by an infant, no part of an indoor distribution board shall be less than 1,2 m above the floor level and no part of an outdoor distribution board shall be less than 0,2 m above the ground level.

Regulation 6.6.1.7

A distribution board shall not be mounted

a) in a bathroom, unless it conforms to certain standards,

b) above a fixed cooking appliance unless it conforms to certain standards,

c) within a radius of 1 m from a water tap or valve (in the same room) unless it conforms to certain standards.

Regulation 6.6.1.18

If an installation is likely to be extended, a distribution board with spare ways should be fitted.

Regulation 6.6.1.19

Each unoccupied opening of a distribution board shall be fitted with a blanking plate.

Regulation 6.6.1.20

Unless obvious, permanent labelling shall identify all incoming and outgoing circuits of the distribution board.

inadvertent: *not resulting from or achieved through intentional planning*

6.1.5 Wiring of subcircuits

We are going to learn about the wiring of the following subcircuits in a domestic electrical installation:

- Stove subcircuits.
- Geyser subcircuits.
- Socket outlet (plug) subcircuit.
- Lighting subcircuits.
- Bell subcircuits.

Stove subcircuit

A stove circuit is also known as a cooking appliance circuit.

Figure 6.7 shows the wiring diagram for a stove circuit.

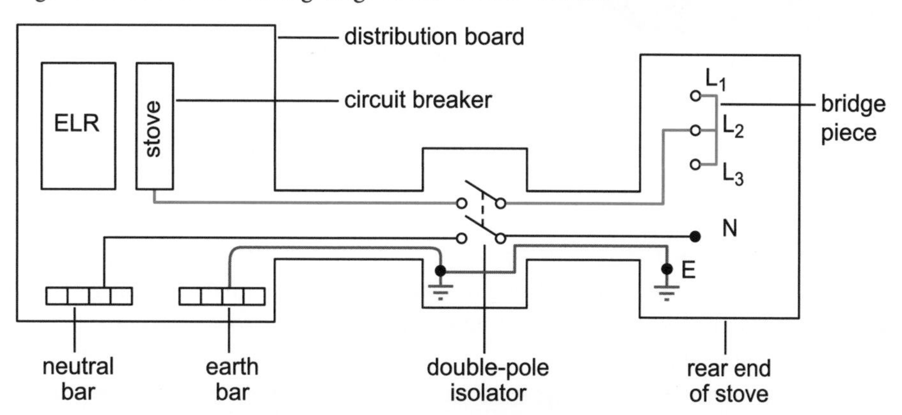

Figure 6.7: Stove subcircuit

The following are some relevant regulations from SANS 10142-1 concerning cooking appliance circuits.

Regulation 6.16.3 | Cooking appliances

Note: Cooking appliances include built-in stoves, oven hobs and the like.

Regulation 6.16.3.1.1

The circuit that supplies a cooking appliance through fixed wiring, a stove coupler, or an industrial-type socket outlet shall have a readily accessible switch disconnector. The switch disconnector may supply more than one appliance.

Regulation 6.16.3.1.2

A switch disconnector for a cooking appliance(s) shall

a) be in the same room as the appliance(s),
b) be at a height above floor level of not less than 0,5 m and not more than 2,2 m,
c) preferably not be above the cooking appliance(s),
d) be within 3 m of the appliance(s), but within 0,5 m of the appliance(s) if the switch disconnector's purpose is not clearly indicated, and
e) not be fixed to the appliance.

Regulation 6.16.3.2.1

A dedicated circuit(s) shall be provided for cooking appliance(s) that are rated at more than 16 A.

Regulation 6.16.3.2.2

One circuit shall not supply more than one permanently connected cooking appliance, unless the appliances are in the same room.

Regulation 6.16.3.2.3

A cooking appliance circuit may also supply one socket outlet if the rating of the socket outlet does not exceed 16 A and if the following are all contained in one control unit:

a) the socket outlet;
b) an earth leakage protection device including overcurrent protection for protecting the socket outlet; and
c) the switch disconnector required for the cooking appliance.

Activity 6.1

1. State four functions of IEC symbols. (4)
2. Draw the IEC symbols for the following:
   2.1 Variable resistor.
   2.2 Bell.
   2.3 Earth connection. (3 × 1 = 3)
3. What is a distribution board? (4)
4. Make a neat and fully labelled drawing to show the internal wiring of a distribution board where an ELR is used as the main-switch disconnector. (6)
5. Complete the table below.

Subcircuit	Component	Size	Conductor size
	Main switch		
	Earth leakage		
Stove (cooking appliance)	Circuit breaker		
Geyser	Circuit breaker		
Socket outlet	Circuit breaker		
Lights	Circuit breaker		
Bell	Circuit breaker		

(14)

6. Make a neat and fully labelled drawing of a stove subcircuit. (5)
7. What does the SANS: 10142-1 state with regard to cooking appliances rated at more than 16 A? (2)
8. What does the SANS: 10142-1 state with regard to a circuit supplying more than one permanently connected cooking appliance? (2)

TOTAL: [40]

Geyser subcircuit

A ***geyser*** is used to heat water and store heated water. It has a heating element and the action of this heating element is controlled by a ***thermostat***. The function of the thermostat is to electrically disconnect the heating element from the supply when the water has reached the desired temperature.

Figure 6.8 shows the wiring diagram for a geyser circuit.

geyser: *domestic gas or electric water heater with a storage tank*

thermostat: *device that regulates the temperature in a heating device*

bonded: *electrically joined together*

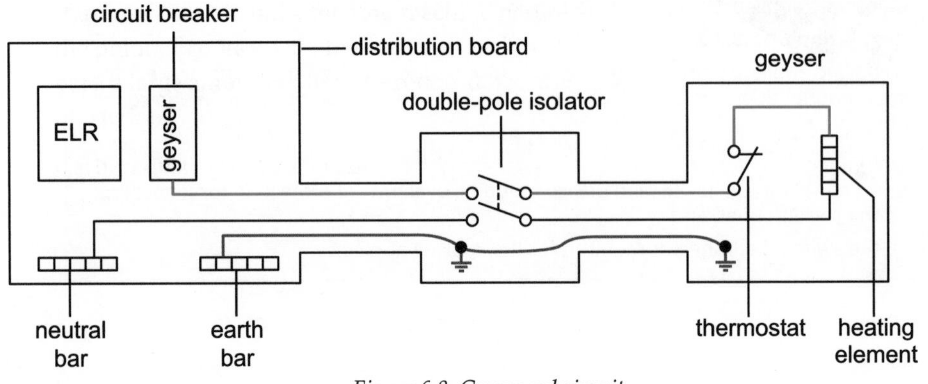

Figure 6.8: Geyser subcircuit

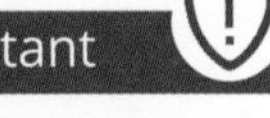

Important

- Geysers do not have to be protected by earth leakage protection.
- If a geyser is to be installed in a bathroom, it must be protected by an earth leakage device.

The following are some relevant regulations from SANS 10142-1 concerning geyser circuits.

Regulation 6.16.2 | Water heaters

Note: Water heaters include geysers, instantaneous water heaters including units for boiling water.

Regulation 6.16.2.1

All water heaters shall be ***bonded***.

Regulation 6.16.2.2

Dedicated circuits shall be provided for water heaters and there may be more than one water heater on each circuit.

Regulation 6.9.3.1 | Disconnecting devices

An appliance or equipment that is not supplied from a socket outlet, including equipment automatically or remote controlled, shall be capable of being disconnected from the supply by an easily accessible switch disconnector. The disconnector shall be mounted

a) within arm's reach from the terminals of the appliance, or
b) in a distribution board, if the device is capable of being locked in the open position.

The disconnector can control more than one appliance if the functions of the appliances are related.

Regulation 3.4 | Definition of arm's reach

Arm's reach is the volume that is limited by the relevant of the following distances measured from a surface expected to be occupied by persons:

a) 2,5 m vertically upwards;
b) 1,25 m vertically downwards from the outer edge of the surface;
c) 1,25 m horizontally outwards from the outer edges of the surface; and
d) 0,75 m horizontally inwards from the outer edges of the surface and underneath the surface.

Socket outlet or plug subcircuit

Regulation 3.72 | Definition of socket outlet

A socket outlet is a device that

a) has two or more metallic spring contacts designed to accept the corresponding pins of a plug,
b) is designed for fixing onto or into a building element or other flat surface, and
c) is arranged for connection to the wiring of an installation.

Figure 6.9 shows the wiring diagram for a socket outlet subcircuit (plug subcircuit).

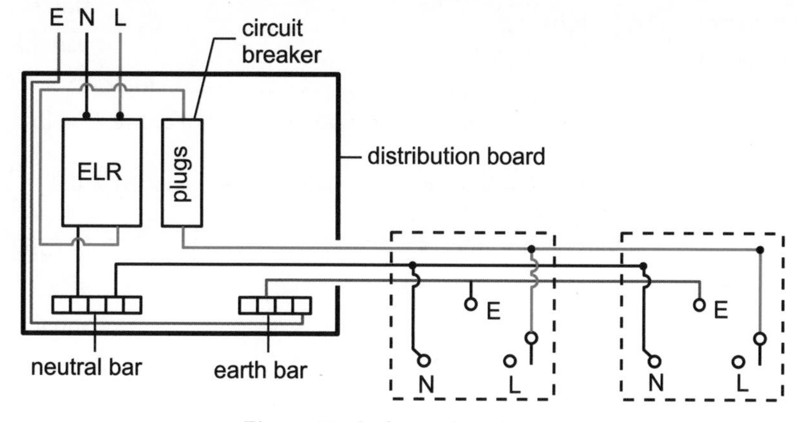

Figure 6.9: Socket outlet subcircuit

The following are some relevant regulations concerning socket outlets (plugs).

Regulation 6.15 | Socket outlets

Note: Earth leakage protection on socket outlets is compulsory except where specified otherwise.

Regulation 6.15.1.1.4

Note 1: ***Dedicated socket outlets*** are the only socket outlets that need not be protected by earth leakage.

Regulation 6.15.3

Single-phase circuits that only supply socket outlets rated at not more than 16 A,

a) shall have overcurrent protection;

b) shall use conductors that are rated at not less than 16 A.

Regulation 6.15.6.1

A socket outlet that is exposed to the weather (or to the condensation, dripping, splashing or accumulation of water) shall be of a weatherproof type.

Regulation 6.15.6.2

A floor-mounted socket outlet (recessed or not) shall be so mounted that

a) the floor can be cleaned or washed without the insulation resistance of the installation being affected, and

b) there is no risk of live parts touching any floor covering used.

Regulation 6.15.6.3

A socket outlet shall not be installed within a radius of 2 m of a water tap (in the same room) unless the socket outlet

a) has earth leakage protection, or

b) is connected to a safety supply.

dedicated socket outlet: *an outlet that supplies power to one device or appliance*

Lighting subcircuits

The lighting subcircuits are the more difficult circuits to wire. There are many types of wiring diagrams that we must know, such as:

- Lights controlled from one point (one-way switching).
- Lights controlled from two points (two-way switching).
- Lights controlled from three or four points (intermediate switching).

The following are some relevant regulations from SANS 10142-1 concerning lighting.

Regulation 6.14 | Lighting

Regulation 6.14.1.1

A single-phase circuit that supplies ***luminaires*** only can supply any number of luminaires.

Regulation 6.14.4.2

The outer contact of an ***Edison-screw-type*** lamp holder shall be connected to the neutral conductor.

luminaire: *a complete lighting unit consisting of one or more electric lamps with all of the necessary parts and wiring*

Edison-screw-type lamp: *standard lightbulb having a right-hand threaded metal base which screws into a matching threaded socket*

switch: *device that controls the flow of current by making or breaking the flow of current*

Figure 6.10: Edison-screw-type lamps

Table 6.3 shows the different types of light switches available.

Table 6.3: Types of light switches

Description	Front view	Rear view	Simplified rear view
Single-lever one-way switch			
Two-lever one-way switch			
Three-lever one-way switch			
Single-lever two-way switch			
Single-lever intermediate switch			

Important 

- One-way switches have a coloured marking. In some cases when the coloured marking is visible, it means that the switch is on. In some cases when the end with the coloured marking is raised, it means that the switch is on.
- Two-way and intermediate switches have no visible markings. This means that they can be on or off in either position

One-way switching

This method of switching is used to control one light or many lights from one position only. Lights are always connected in parallel with one another. The reasons for this are the following:

- When one light stops working, the others will continue working.
- The voltage drop across each light will be the same.

Figure 6.11 shows the wiring diagram for one-way switching.

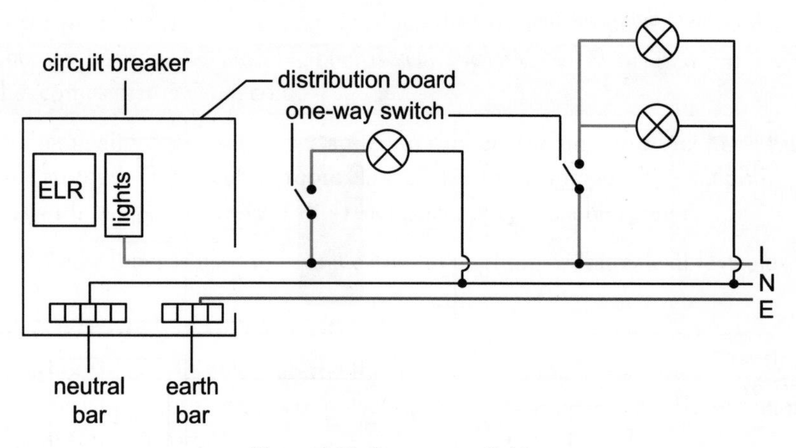

Figure 6.11: One-way switching

Two-way switching

Two-way switching is used to control a single light or a bank of lights from two different points, such as:

- In a long passage.
- In a room with two entrances.
- At a staircase.

Figure 6.12 shows the wiring diagram for two-way switching.

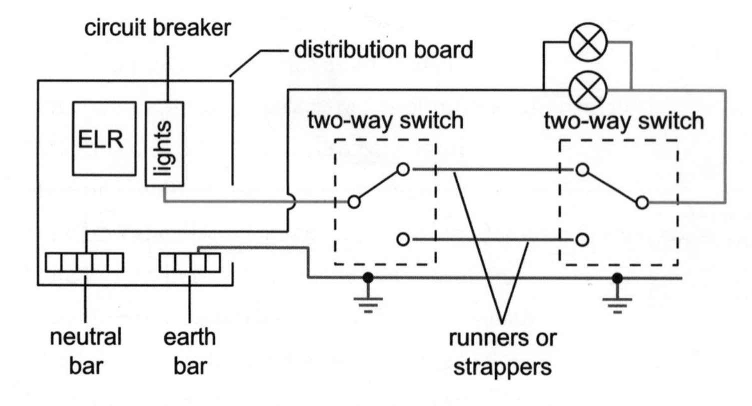

Figure 6.12: Two-way switching

Intermediate switching

Intermediate switching is used to control a single light or a bank of lights from three or four points.

Figures 6.13a and 6.13b show wiring diagrams for intermediate switching.

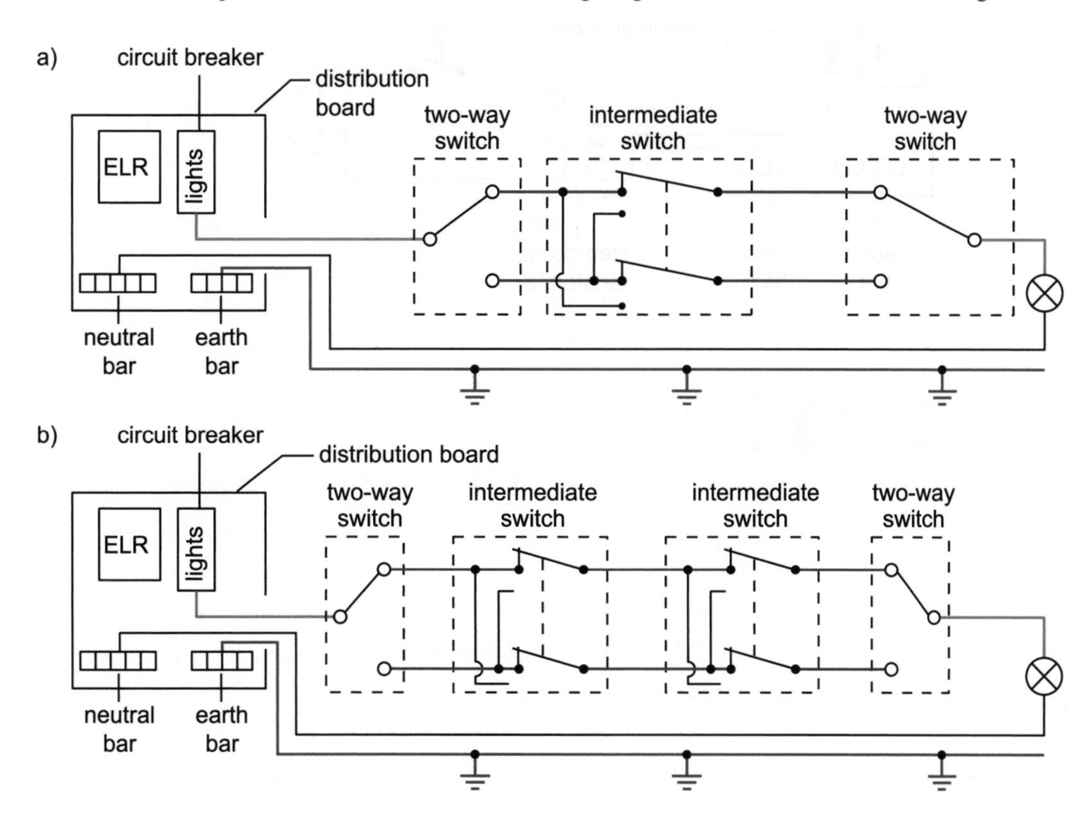

Figure 6.13a and 6.13b: Intermediate switching

Bell subcircuit

There are three types of doorbell systems:

1. A battery-operated system (batteries need to be replaced).
2. A bell system operated at 220 V.
3. A bell system operated via a step-down transformer.

Figures 6.14a and 6.14b show the subcircuit wiring diagrams for a bell.

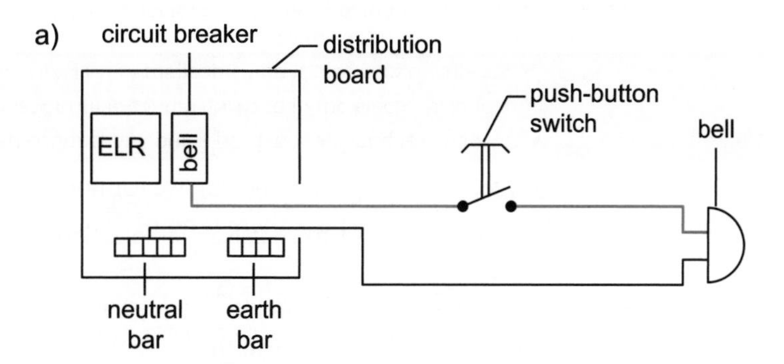

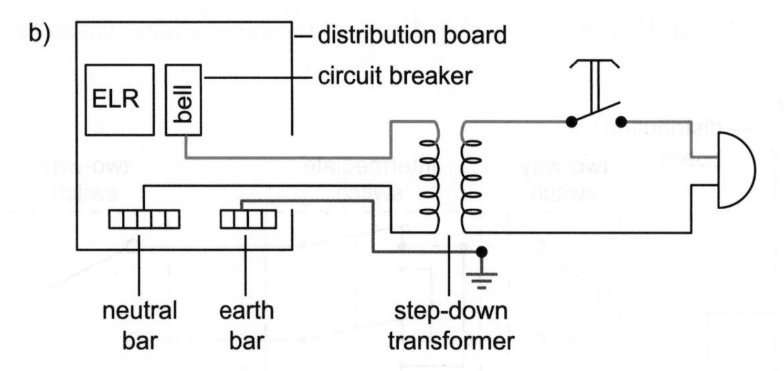

Figure 6.14a and 6.14b: Bell circuits

Activity 6.2

1. What does the SANS 10142-1 state about the following with regard to geysers (water heaters)?
   - 1.1 Bonding. (2)
   - 1.2 A circuit for a geyser. (2)
2. Draw a neat and fully labelled circuit diagram of a geyser subcircuit. (6)
3. What does the SANS 10142-1 state with regard to the following?
   - 3.1 Earth leakage protection for socket outlets. (2)
   - 3.2 Earth leakage protection for dedicated socket outlets. (2)
4. Draw a neat and fully labelled circuit diagram of a socket outlet subcircuit. Your diagram must include two socket outlets. (6)
5. What does the SANS 10142-1 state with regard to the following?
   - 5.1 The number of luminaires supplied by a circuit. (2)
   - 5.2 The outer contact of an Edison-screw-type lamp holder. (2)
   - 5.3 The three places in an installation where two-way switching is used. (3)
6. Make a neat and fully labelled drawing of a lighting subcircuit in which one light is controlled from two different points. (7)
7. Make a neat and fully labelled drawing of a bell circuit that has a step-down transformer. (6)

TOTAL: [40]

Unit 6.2: Protective devices for electrical installations

Electricity is a very dangerous form of energy, yet one that we cannot do without. When it is treated with care and respect, there is no need to fear electricity.

All electrical work to any electrical installation must conform to the regulations contained in the SANS 10142-1: 2020. The purpose of these regulations is to ensure protection of people, animals, circuits, appliances and equipment.

In Module 1, we learned about isolating circuits for repair and about some of the safety switches used in electrical installations. In this unit we will explore the possible dangers of electricity and how we further safeguard against them.

6.2.1 Protection against leakage current

Leakage current threatens human and animal life. To safeguard against the harmful effects of leakage current, an electrical installation must be earthed.

point of consumption: *the point in any electrical installation where electrical energy is converted into another form of energy*

Definition of earthing

Earthing means electrically connecting all ***points of consumption***, switches and all exposed (conductive parts) of an installation to the general mass of the earth.

Earth has a zero potential (that is, it has no charge). It will therefore accept any leakage current and make this fault current harmless (we cannot make the earth 'live', no matter how much current we feed into it).

The purpose of earthing, therefore, is to protect human and animal life against the harmful effect of leakage current, static charges and lightning discharges.

You will notice that there is no chance of electrocution as long as the earthing system is present and effective. The danger of electrocution will arise as soon as the earthing system is not working properly, which is why we need earth leakage relays.

Earth leakage relay

We first encountered earth leakage relays (ELRs) in Module 1.

Regulation 3.30 | Definition of earth leakage unit

An earth leakage unit is a device that is capable of detecting the flow of a specified or predetermined current from a circuit to earth, and of disconnecting, automatically and reliably, the affected circuit within a specified time when such current exceeds the specified or predetermined value.

This description can be difficult to understand, so let's try to simplify it:

The function of an ELR is to automatically disconnect an electrical installation from the supply if a leakage current exceeds a certain value.

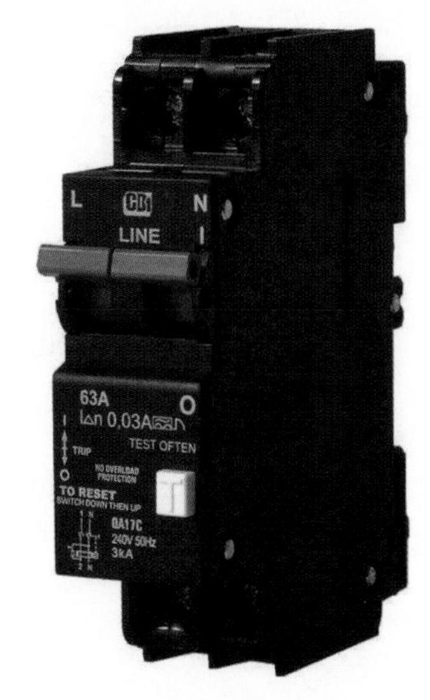

Figure 6.15: A single-phase earth leakage relay

6.2.2 Protection against overcurrents

Every installation, circuit and appliance must be protected against the harmful effects of overcurrents. Overcurrents occur as a result of overloads and short circuits:

- An **overload** occurs when a circuit is required to carry more current than it was designed for. The overload could be anything from small values to large overcurrents.
- A **short circuit** occurs when the live conductor touches the neutral in the case of a single-phase system.

Overloads are not a serious fault condition but over a period of time they will cause damage. Short circuits, on the other hand, are very serious faults because they produce extremely large fault currents which will destroy circuits almost instantly.

Circuit breakers and fuses

We had a brief look at circuit breakers and fuses in Module 1.

Circuit breakers and fuses are used to offer protection against overcurrents. Their function is to automatically disconnect the load from the supply in the event of an overload or a short circuit.

Regulation 3.12 | Definition of circuit breaker

A circuit breaker is a mechanical switching device that is capable of making, carrying and breaking currents under normal circuit conditions and of making, carrying for a specified time, and automatically breaking currents under specified abnormal circuit conditions such as those of overcurrent.

Regulation 3.42 | Definition of fuse

A fuse is a device that, by the melting of one or more of its specifically designed and dimensioned elements, opens the circuit in which it is inserted if the current that flows through it exceeds the rated current for a specified time.

Circuit breakers and fuses have two ratings, namely overload and short-circuit ratings.

- **Overload rating**
  This is the maximum current that will be able to flow through a circuit breaker or fuse before it will open/break the circuit, e.g. 10 A; 20 A; 30 A.
- **Short-circuit rating**
  This is the maximum fault current that a circuit breaker or fuse is capable of interrupting, e.g. 1 kA; 2,5 kA; 5 kA.

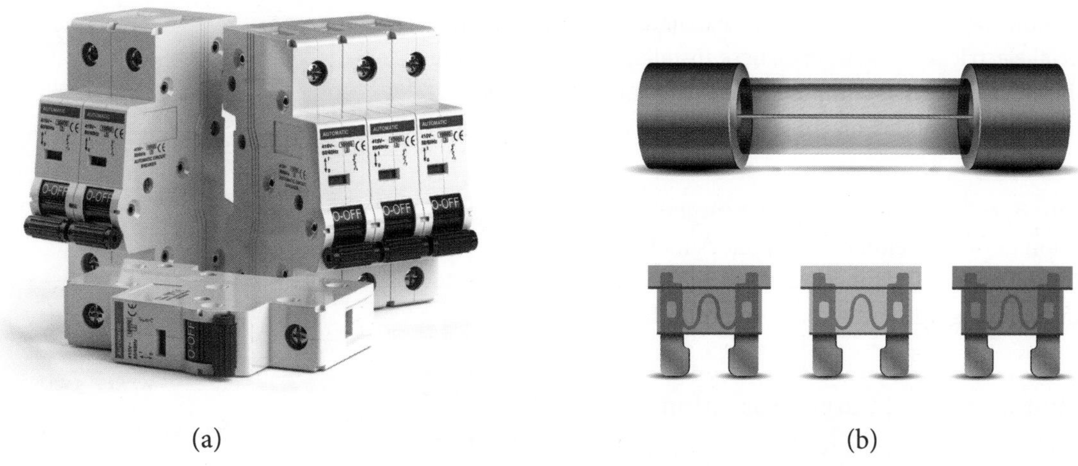

Figure 6.16: (a) Circuit breakers and (b) fuses

6.2.3 Protection against voltage surges

Overhead lines need to be protected against the harmful effects of voltage surges caused mainly by lightning.

transient: *lasting only for a short time*

Most faults on overhead lines are caused by ***transient*** voltages or voltage surges. This means that the surges will disappear from the system very rapidly. But they may produce a flashover between phases or between a phase and earth. A flashover is a high-voltage electric short circuit made through the air between exposed conductors.

Lightning arrestors

Lightning arrestors are used to protect overhead lines and insulators against flashovers. Voltage surges or transient voltages are trapped by a lightning arrestor and directed to ground immediately.

Figure 6.17: Lightning arrestors

Low-voltage surge protectors

It is possible for voltage surges to cause damage in domestic and industrial electrical installations. These installations often include sensitive devices such as computers, television sets, decoders, modems, servers and fax machines that can be easily destroyed by surges.

Installations can be protected against surges by installing surge protection devices in either the supplier's meter box or the distribution board. The function of a surge protection device is to trap any voltage surge and direct it to ground immediately.

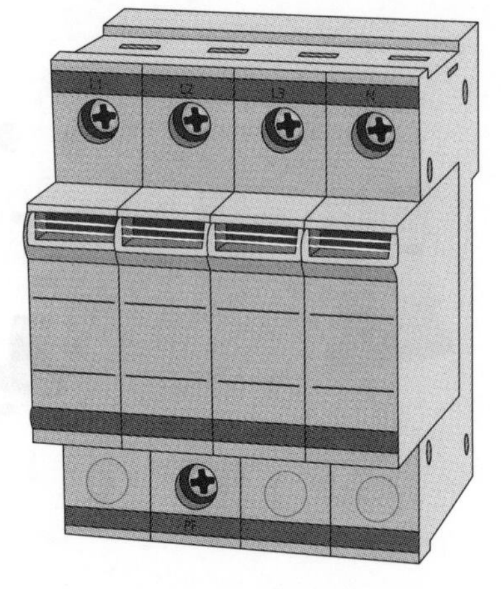

Figure 6.18: Surge protection device

Regulation 6.7.6.1 | Surge protection

A surge protection device (SPD) may be installed to protect an installation against transient overvoltages and surge currents, such as those caused by switching operations or induced by atmospheric discharges (lightning).

Activity 6.3

1. What does earthing mean? (4)
2. What is the purpose of earthing? (3)
3. State the function of an earth leakage relay. (3)
4. State two causes of overcurrents. (2)
5. State the function of circuit breakers and fuses. (3)
6. State the function of a surge protector. (3)
7. Name two places in a domestic installation where surge protection devices can be installed. (2)

TOTAL: [20]

Summary of Module 6

We have covered the following in this module. See if you have mastered each of these sections.

Unit 6.1 Wiring domestic electrical installations

- All electrical drawings or wiring diagrams contain standard IEC symbols.
- The supply authority supplies electrical energy to an electrical installation using one of the following methods:
  - Aerial conductors connected to an overhead transmission line.
  - An underground cable connected to an overhead transmission line.
  - An underground cable connected to a distribution transformer.
- The supplier's meter box is mounted outside the house on the wall closest to the point of electrical entry.
- A distribution board is an electrical enclosure that contains electrical equipment for the distribution or control of electrical power from one or more incoming circuits to one or more outgoing circuits.
- Each distribution board is controlled by a switch disconnector.
- Unless it is obvious, permanent labelling identifies all incoming and outgoing circuits of the distribution board.
- The circuit that supplies a cooking appliance through fixed wiring, a stove coupler or an industrial-type socket outlet should have a readily accessible switch disconnector. The switch disconnector may supply more than one appliance, but then the appliances must be in the same room.
- A geyser has a heating element and its action is controlled by a thermostat.
- All water heaters should be bonded.
- Dedicated circuits should be provided for water heaters and there may be more than one heater on each circuit.
- Cooking appliances, geysers and lights do not have to be protected by an earth leakage relay.
- If a geyser is to be installed in a bathroom, it must be protected by an earth leakage device.
- Earth leakage protection on socket outlets is compulsory, except where specified otherwise.
- Dedicated socket outlets are the only socket outlets that do not have to be protected by earth leakage.
- A single-phase circuit that supplies luminaires only can supply any number of luminaires.
- The outer contact of an Edison-screw-type lamp holder should be connected to the neutral conductor.

Unit 6.2 Protective devices for electrical installations

- Leakage current threatens human and animal life. To safeguard against the harmful effects of leakage current, an electrical installation must be earthed.
- Earthing means electrically connecting an object to the general mass of the earth.
- The purpose of earthing is to protect human and animal life against the harmful effects of leakage current, static charges and lightning discharges.
- The function of an earth leakage relay is to automatically disconnect an installation from the supply if a leakage current exceeds a certain value.
- Every installation, circuit and appliance must be protected against the harmful effects of overcurrents.
- Overcurrents occur as a result of overloads and short circuits.
- Circuit breakers and fuses are used to offer protection against overcurrents.
- Circuit breakers and fuses have two ratings, namely overload and short-circuit ratings.
- Fuses are the simplest and most economical protective devices used to protect circuits against overcurrents caused by overloads and short circuits.
- Lightning arrestors are used to protect overhead lines and insulators against flashovers.
- Voltage surges or transient voltages are trapped by a lightning arrestor and directed to ground immediately.
- Domestic and industrial electrical installations can be protected against surges by installing surge protection devices in either the supplier's meter box or the distribution board.
- The function of a surge protection device is to trap any voltage surge and direct it to ground immediately.

Summative Assessment for Module 6

1. Draw the IEC symbol for the following:
   - 1.1 Push-button switch.
   - 1.2 Conductors join.
   - 1.3 Fuse.
   - 1.4 Circuit breaker.
   - 1.5 Two-way switch. (5 × 1 = 5)
2. State three methods used by the supply authority to supply electrical energy to an electrical installation. (3)
3. State three reasons why some municipalities are relocating the energy meters into electrical kiosks found outside the consumer's property. (3)
4. What does the SANS: 10142-1 state with regard to the following?
   - 4.1 Labelling of distribution boards.
   - 4.2 Unoccupied openings of a distribution board. (4)
5. What is the function of the thermostat found in a geyser? (1)
6. What does the SANS: 10142-1 state with regard to the following?
   - 6.1 Socket outlets near a tap. (4)
   - 6.2 Socket outlets exposed to the weather. (3)
7. Draw a neat and fully labelled circuit diagram of a lighting subcircuit showing how a light can be controlled from three points. (7)
8. Why are electrical systems connected to earth? (4)
9. State when the following faults will occur:
   - 9.1 An overload. (3)
   - 9.2 A short circuit. (3)
10. Explain what is meant by:
    - 10.1 Overload rating of a circuit breaker. (2)
    - 10.2 Short-circuit rating of a circuit breaker. (2)
11. What is the main cause of voltage surges in transmission lines? (1)

TOTAL: [45]

Testing a single-phase installation

Module

7

lessor: *a person who leases or lets a property to another; a landlord*

Overview of Module 7

In South Africa, it is a statutory requirement that every user or ***lessor*** of an electrical installation shall have a valid Certificate of Compliance (CoC) for every such installation. A CoC is issued by a registered person only after inspection and testing of the installation.

In this module we are going to learn how to conduct four important tests on a single-phase installation.

When you have completed this module, you should be able to:

Unit 7.1: Testing of a single-phase installation

- Describe fully how the following tests are conducted:
  - Continuity of bonding test.
  - Polarity test.
  - Insulation resistance test between conductors.
  - Insulation resistance test between conductors and earth.

Figure 7.1: Conducting the insulation resistance test

Starter activity

Discuss the following in class:

- You need to determine whether a conductor is broken or not. All you have is a multimeter. Do you think that this instrument would be of any assistance?
- The purpose of insulation is to electrically separate conductors. How would you be able to determine that there is no damaged insulation between conductors run in a conduit pipe?
- Why do you think it is necessary to establish that only the live conductors are broken by ***single-pole switches***?

single-pole switch: *a switch that has only one set of contacts*

Unit 7.1: Testing of a single-phase installation

Inspection and testing of all electrical installations are required by law. The purpose of testing is to ensure that all components have been installed and connected correctly and that the installation poses no danger to people, animals, equipment or appliances.

If the installation complies with strict standards, a registered person issues a Certificate of Compliance (CoC) for the installation along with a test report.

Regulation 3.9 | Definition of Certificate of Compliance

A Certificate of Compliance (CoC) is issued by a registered person in respect of an electrical installation or part of an electrical installation.

Regulation 8.1 | Inspection and tests

Section 5.4 of the test report provides for the person who carried out the inspection and testing of the electrical installation as given in 8.6 and 8.7, if the results are acceptable, to verify that the installation complies with the requirement of this part of SANS 10142-1.

Regulation 8.6.1 | Testing (General)

Note: Conduct all tests and complete a copy of 'Section 4: Tests' for each distribution board and supply.

In the case of failure in any test, the test shall be repeated after the fault has been rectified. Other tests that might have been influenced by the fault shall also be repeated.

Measuring instruments shall be accurate to within 5% or better.

Insulation resistance tester (Megger)

An ***insulation resistance tester*** is used to conduct the electrical tests explained in this module. An insulation resistance tester (megaohmmeter) is a special type of ohmmeter used to measure very high resistances such as that of insulators.

insulation resistance tester: *measuring instrument designed to measure the resistance of insulators; also called a megaohmmeter*

There are two categories of insulation resistance testers (commonly known by a brand name, Megger):

- Electronic type, which is battery operated (can be digital or analogue).
- Manual type, which is hand-driven.

An analogue insulation resistance tester consists of a display with a moving indicator needle that points to the value of the quantity being measured. Digital insulation testers are more modern and more accurate. They display a reading in numeric form on a liquid crystal screen.

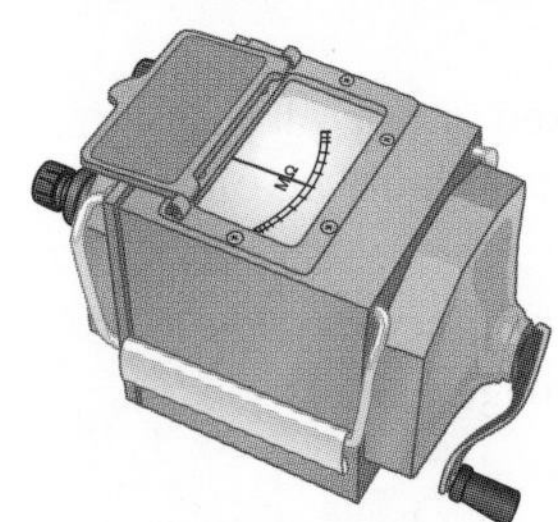

(a) Hand driven

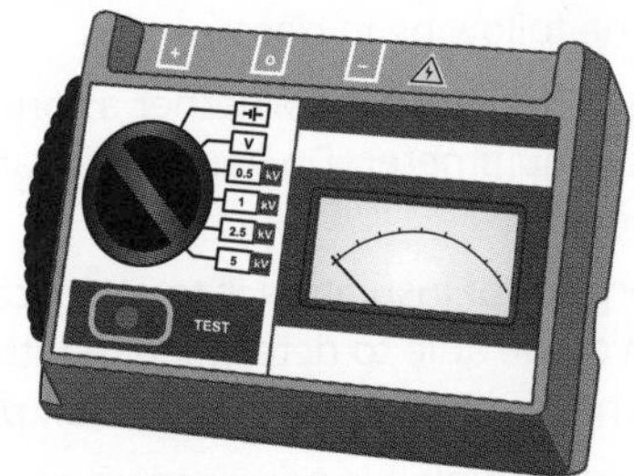

(b) Electronic (analogue)

(c) Electronic (digital)

Figure 7.2: Insulation resistance testers

Note

You can also conduct the tests in this module using a **multifunction tester**. A multifunction tester is a testing device designed to perform multiple tests on installations (including insulation resistance tests).

You can conduct *some* of the tests in this module with a **multimeter**. A multimeter is a popular type of measuring instrument that can measure several basic electrical quantities such as voltage, current and resistance. You will learn more about multimeters in N2.

Any insulation resistance tester can measure any resistance from zero to infinity. Its main purpose, though, is to measure high-resistance values. The instrument has an ohm (Ω) scale. This scale allows for the measurement of low-resistance values and is useful when conducting the continuity test and polarity test.

The mega-ohm scale (MΩ) is used for the measurement of high-resistance values. This scale is used to perform the insulation resistance test. During the testing process using the MΩ scale, a high voltage is produced across the (least) test leads.

In this module, we learn how to conduct the following tests on a single-phase installation:

- Continuity of conductors test.
- Continuity of bonding test.
- Insulation resistance test:
  - Between conductors.
  - Between conductors and earth.
- Polarity test.

7.1.1 Continuity of conductors test

Purpose

To determine whether there are any broken conductors in any circuit.

Instruments used

Any of the following can be used:

- A ***multimeter*** set on the ohm scale.
- A ***Megger*** set on the ohm scale.
- A buzzer or ***bell tester***.

multimeter: *a measuring instrument that can measure more than one electrical quantity*

Megger: *commercial name of an insulation resistance tester*

bell tester: *a simple tester that sounds a bell when it detects continuity*

bridge: *to electrically connect two points*

Procedure

Step 1	The main-switch disconnector must be switched off.
Step 2	All circuit breakers, light switches, isolators and socket outlet switches must be switched on.
Step 3	Remove all bulbs, disconnect all loads (stove, geyser) and unplug all appliances.
Step 4	***Bridge*** the live busbar and the neutral bar (see Figure 7.3).
Step 5	Now test between live and neutral at all points of consumption.
Step 6	The bell tester must sound or the needle of the measuring instrument must deflect towards zero.

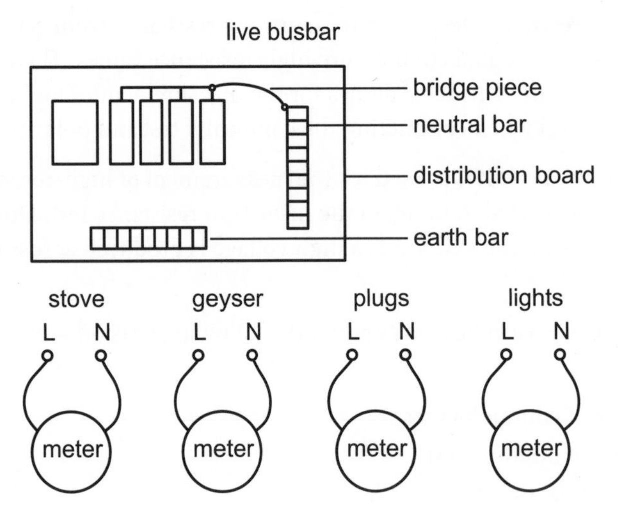

Figure 7.3: Continuity of conductors test

7.1.2 Earth and continuity of bonding test

Regulation 8.6.1 | Continuity of bonding

Test the continuity of the ***bonding*** between the consumer's earth terminal and all exposed conductive parts using a supply that has a no-load DC or AC voltage of 4 V to 24 V, and a current of at least 0,2 A. In each case, the resistance shall not exceed 0,2 Ω.

Regulation 8.6.2 | Resistance of earth continuity conductor

Use a resistance meter to measure the resistance of the earth continuity conductors between the consumer's earth terminal and the earthing terminals of all points of consumption and switches. The values shall not exceed those given in Table 8.1 [SANS 10142-1: 2020].

bonding: *electrically joined together*

Purpose

To ensure that the consumer's earth terminal (earth bar) is electrically connected to all exposed conductive parts, the earthing terminals of all points of consumption and the switches of an installation.

Instruments used

Any of the following can be used:

- A multimeter set on the ohm scale.
- A Megger set on the ohm scale.
- A buzzer or bell tester.

Procedure

Step	Action
Step 1	Attach a long conductor to one of the leads of the instrument.
Step 2	Now touch the end of this long conductor to the other lead and zero the meter.
Step 3	Clip the normal lead onto the consumer's earth bar and then touch the end of the long conductor to all the conductive parts of the installation.
Step 4	Record the readings.

Conductive parts of an installation

- Hot- and cold-water pipes (copper).
- Geyser.
- Stove.
- Plugs and light switches.
- Metal roofs.
- Gutters and downpipes.

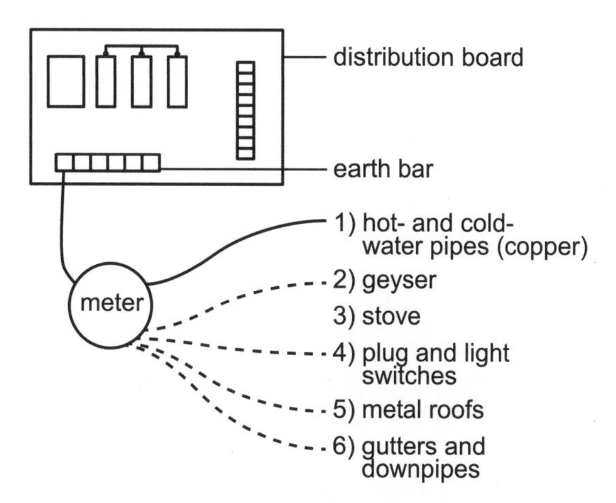

Figure 7.4: Earth and continuity of bonding test

7.1.3 Insulation resistance tests

Regulation 8.6.8 | Insulation resistance

Note: Before power is connected to any new or altered circuit, the test for insulation resistance should be carried out to ensure there is no short circuit or high impedance faults in the installation, and that it is safe to energise.

Regulation 8.6.8.1

When carrying out insulation resistance tests,

a) use an AC or DC voltage of at least twice the nominal voltage, with a minimum of 500 V;

b) ensure that all fuses are in place and switches and circuit breakers are in the closed position. Loads may be disconnected.

Note: To prevent damage, ensure that voltage-sensitive electronic equipment, such as dimmer switches, touch switches, time delay devices, power controllers, electronic starters for fluorescent lamps, earth leakage units, surge arresters and certain appliances, are disconnected so that they are not subjected to the test voltage.

Regulation 8.6.8.2

The insulation resistance, measured as follows, shall be at least 1,0 MΩ:

a) to measure the insulation resistance to earth, apply the test voltage between the earth continuity conductor and the whole system of live conductors, or any section of it;

and

b) to measure the insulation resistance between the conductors, apply the test voltage
   1. between the phase conductors and, when relevant,
   2. between the phase conductors and the neutral conductor.

See it online

Insulation resistance test
Watch the test being performed in this video – How to do an Insulation Resistance Test on a Single Phase Installation by Shukela Training | https://youtu.be/_-n6BiFJy8w

Insulation resistance test between conductors

Purpose

To ensure that all conductors are electrically separated from one another.

Instruments used

Any of the following can be used:

- Insulation resistance tester.
- Megger.

Procedure

Step 1	Ensure that: 1.1 The main-switch disconnector is off. 1.2 All circuit breakers, switches and isolators are on. 1.3 All loads are disconnected. 1.4 All bulbs have been removed. 1.5 All appliances are unplugged.
Step 2	Connect one lead of the Megger to the live busbar and the other lead to the neutral bar (see Figure 7.5).
Step 3	Depress the test button. The minimum allowable reading must be 1 MΩ.

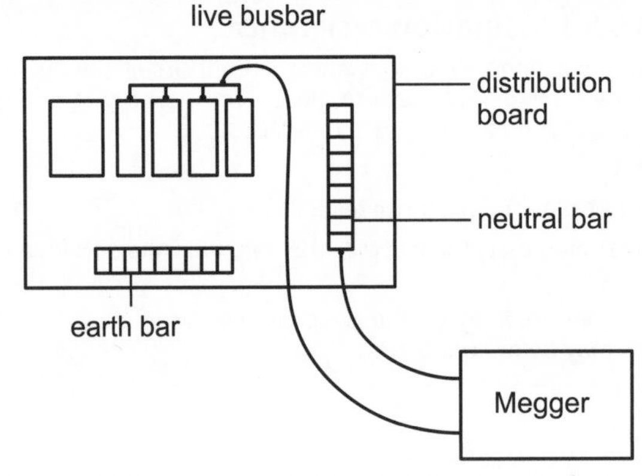

Figure 7.5: Insulation resistance test between conductors

Insulation resistance test between conductors and earth

Purpose

To ensure that all conductors are electrically separated from earth.

Instruments used

Any of the following can be used:

- Insulation resistance tester.
- Megger.

Procedure

Step 1	Ensure that: 1.1 The main-switch disconnector is off. 1.2 All circuit breakers, switches and isolators are on. 1.3 All loads are disconnected. 1.4 All bulbs have been removed. 1.5 All appliances are unplugged.
Step 2	Connect one lead to the earth bar and the other lead to the live busbar (see Figure 7.6). Depress the test button. The minimum allowable reading must be 1 MΩ.
Step 3	Now move the lead from the live busbar to the neutral bar and repeat the test.

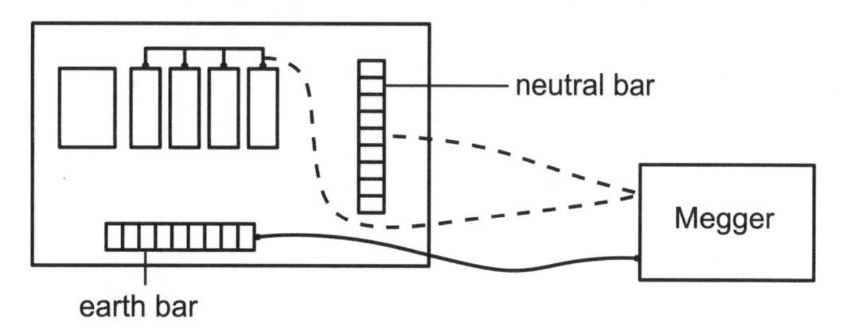

Figure 7.6: Insulation resistance test between conductors and earth

7.1.4 Polarity test

Regulation 8.6.13 | Polarity at points of consumption

Ensure that:

a) all single-pole switching devices, fuses and circuit breakers have been connected in the phase conductor,

b) the phase terminals in fixed appliances and in all single-phase socket outlets have been connected to the phase conductor,

c) the centre contact of each Edison-screw lamp holder is connected to the phase conductor.

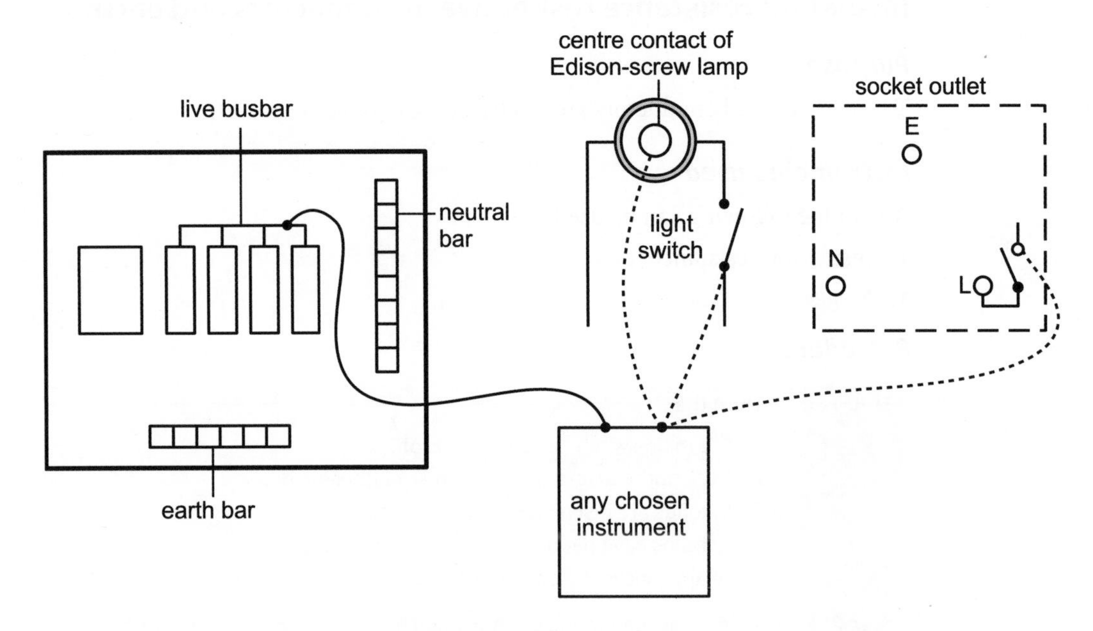

Figure 7.6: Polarity test

Purpose

To ensure that all single-pole switches, fuses and circuit breakers break only the live conductor and that the centre contact of each Edison-screw lamp holder is connected to the live conductor.

Instruments used

Any of the following can be used:

- A multimeter set on the ohm scale.
- A Megger set on the ohm scale.
- A bell tester.
- A buzzer.

Procedure

Step 1	Ensure that: 1.1 The main-switch disconnector is off. 1.2 All circuit breakers are on. 1.3 All Edison-screw-type bulbs have been removed.
Step 2	Connect one lead to the live busbar and the other lead to: 2.1 The incoming side of the light switches. 2.2 The incoming side of the switch of switched socket outlets. 2.3 The centre pin of the Edison-screw lamp holders.
Step 3	In each case, the buzzer must sound or the needle of the multimeter must deflect towards zero. This tells us that the phase conductors are broken by the switches.

Activity 7.1

1. Who is allowed to issue a Certificate of Compliance? (1)
2. What procedure must be followed should an installation fail any test? (4)
3. State three instruments that can be used to conduct the continuity of conductors test. (3)
4. State the purpose of the earth and continuity of bonding test. (4)
5. Name five conductive parts of an installation. (5)
6. State the maximum resistance that an earth continuity conductor between the consumer's earth terminal and the earthing terminals of all points of consumption and switches is allowed to have. (1)
7. State the maximum resistance that the bonding conductor between the consumer's earth terminal and all exposed conductive parts of the installation is allowed to have. (1)
8. What is the minimum allowable insulation resistance value? (1)
9. What is the purpose of the insulation resistance test between conductors? (2)
10. State the procedure that is used to conduct the insulation resistance test between conductors. (7)
11. State the purpose of the polarity test. (4)
12. Name two instruments that are used to conduct the polarity test. (2)

TOTAL: [35]

Summary of Module 7

We have covered the following in this module. See if you have mastered each of these sections.

Unit 7.1 Testing of a single-phase installation

- A Certificate of Compliance is issued by a registered person in respect of an electrical installation or part of an electrical installation.
- In the case of failure in any test, the test shall be repeated after the fault has been rectified. Other tests that might have been influenced by the fault shall also be repeated.
- The continuity of conductors test is conducted in order to determine whether there are broken conductors in any circuit.
- The purpose of the earth and continuity of bonding test is to ensure that the consumer's earth terminal (earth bar) is electrically connected to all exposed conductive parts, the earthing terminals of all points of consumption and switches of an installation.
- The maximum allowable resistance of the bonding continuity conductor is 0,2 Ω.
- The maximum allowable resistance of the earth continuity conductors shall not exceed those values given in Table 8.1 [SANS 10142-1: 2020].
- Before power is connected to any new or altered circuit, the test for insulation resistance should be carried out to ensure that there is no short circuit or high impedance faults in the installation, and that it is safe to energise.
- The minimum insulation resistance value is 1 MΩ.
- The purpose of the polarity test is to ensure that all single-pole switches, fuses and circuit breakers break only the live conductor and that the centre contact of each Edison-screw lamp holder is connected to the live conductor.

Summative assessment for Module 7

1. State what has to be done before a Certificate of Compliance is issued. (2)
2. What is the purpose of the continuity of conductors test? (1)
3. State the procedure that is used to conduct the earth and continuity of bonding test. (4)
4. What does the SANS 10142-1: 2020 state with regard to the insulation resistance test on an installation? (5)
5. Name the instrument that is used to conduct the insulation resistance test. (1)
6. What is the purpose of the insulation resistance test between conductors and earth? (3)
7. State the procedure that is used to conduct the polarity test. (9)

TOTAL: [25]

Magnetism and electromagnetism

Module

8

Overview of Module 8

Magnetism is a force of a magnetic material that attracts or repels other magnetic materials. Magnets are usually made of iron. They are used in earphones, speakers, microwaves, medical equipment and in nearly all appliances that use a motor to make them work. An electromagnet has magnetic properties only when electricity flows through it. Electromagnets are used in the generation of electricity.

In this module we are going to learn about the magnetic effects of electric currents, how electromotive force is induced in a coil or conductor when it interacts with a magnetic field and how an alternating current (AC) waveform is generated.

When you have completed this module, you should be able to:

Unit 8.1: Magnetism

- State the different types of magnets.
- State the characteristics of magnetic lines of flux.
- State how the direction of the magnetic field around a current carrying conductor and coil is determined.

Unit 8.2: Electromagnetism

- State Faraday's laws of electromagnetic induction.
- Describe with the aid of Faraday's law how a sinusoidal wave is generated.
- State the direction of current flow in a DC and AC system.

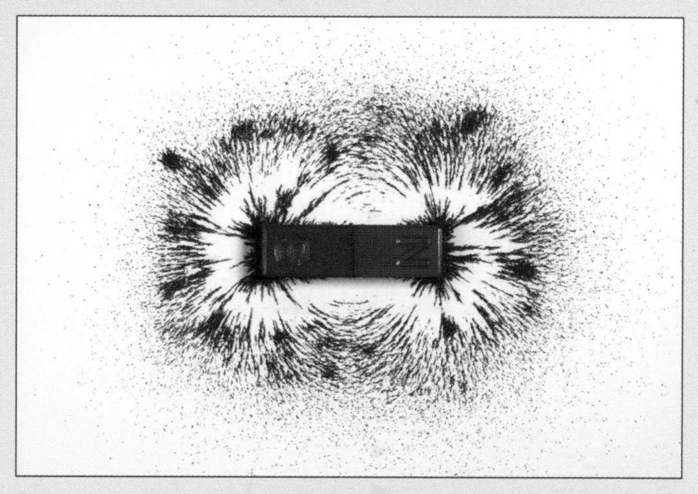

Figure 8.1: Magnet with iron filings showing the magnetic lines of flux

Starter activity

Discuss the following in class:

- You are at the dentist's surgery main gate. You ring the bell for attention. Suddenly you hear a clicking sound and the gate is unlocked. How is this possible?
- Earth has many precious metals. Do you think that we can also find magnets in the ground?
- Do you think that magnets can be used to produce electricity?

Unit 8.1: Magnetism

Magnetism is the force exerted by magnets when they attract or repel each other.

magnetism: *the attractive or repulsive forces exerted by magnets*

magnetic field: *area or region around a magnet in which magnetic forces can be observed*

magnetic flux: *a measurement of the total magnetic field that passes through a given surface*

8.1.1 Magnetic fields

The area or region around any magnet is called a ***magnetic field***. This magnetic field is made up of magnetic field lines as shown in Figure 8.2. Each field line is continuous, forming closed loops. These closed loops are also called magnetic lines of flux or magnetic lines of force.

Definition of magnetic lines of flux (or magnetic lines of force)

Magnetic lines of flux (magnetic field lines) are a visual tool used to represent the shape or patterns of the magnetic field that is found around any magnet.

Magnetic flux is represented by the symbol ϕ (phi) and is measured in webers (Wb).

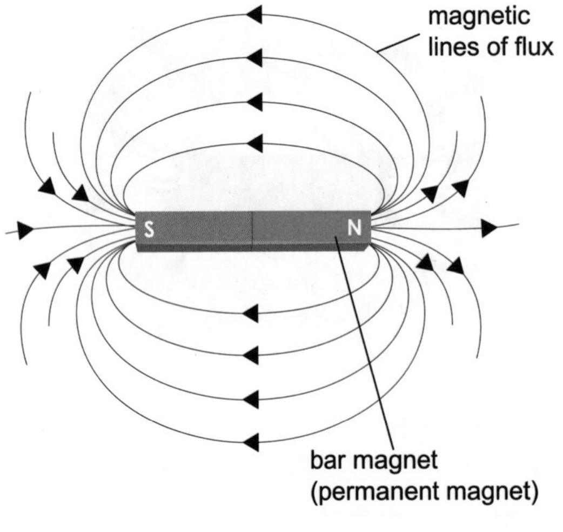

magnetic lines of flux

S N

bar magnet (permanent magnet)

Figure 8.2: Magnetic field around a permanent magnet

See it online 

Magnetism
Watch this experiment online to learn more – Magnets and Magnetism: How do Lines of Magnetic Flux Behave Around a Bar Magnet? By Joe Robinson training | https://youtu.be/LvRiICXoCYs

All magnets have two poles: a north pole and a south pole. The magnetic field is the strongest at these two poles. The north-seeking pole is called the north magnetic pole and the south-seeking pole is called the south magnetic pole. Like poles repel each other (see Figure 8.3a) and unlike poles attract each other (see Figure 8.3b).

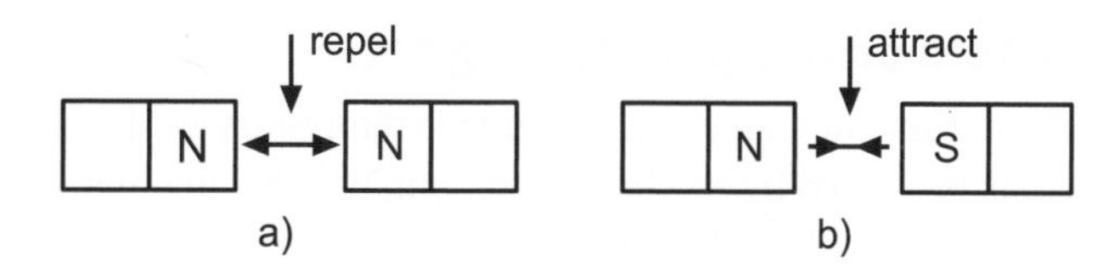

Figure 8.3: (a) Like and (b) unlike poles

Properties of magnetic lines of flux

Magnetic lines of flux have the following characteristics:

- Magnetic lines of flux always flow from the north pole of a magnet to the south pole.
- Magnetic lines of flux always form closed loops.
- They behave like stretched elastic bands, always trying to shorten themselves.
- They never intersect each other.
- Magnetic lines of flux that are parallel and flowing in the same direction will always repel each other.
- Magnetic lines of flux are ***vector*** quantities.

vector: *a quantity that has both direction and magnitude*

electromagnet: *a magnet created when current flows through a coil*

lodestone: *a naturally magnetised mineral that can be used as a magnet*

ferromagnetism: *the mechanism by which certain metals, such as iron, nickel and cobalt, are magnetised by an external magnetic field and retain their magnetism after this field has been removed*

8.1.2 Types of magnets

Magnets can be classified into three types:

- Natural magnets.
- Permanent magnets.
- ***Electromagnets*** (temporary magnets).

Natural magnets

Natural magnets, referred to as ***lodestone*** (or loadstone), are pieces of magnetic or other magnetised minerals that are found buried near the surface of the earth.

Figure 8.4: Lodestone or magnetite

Figure 8.5: A permanent magnet

Permanent magnets

Permanent magnets can be made from iron, nickel and cobalt by exposing them to an external magnetic field. When the external magnetic field is removed, the metal retains its magnetism permanently – a property referred to as ***ferromagnetism***.

Electromagnets or temporary magnets

Unlike a permanent magnet, an electromagnet is temporary in the sense that a magnetic field is produced by an electric current, but this magnetic field disappears as soon as the current is turned off.

core: *a magnetic material with a high* ***permeability*** *used to confine and guide magnetic fields*

permeability: *the ability to support the formation of magnetic fields*

solenoid: *a coil of wire that acts like a magnet when carrying current*

concentric circles: *two or more circles that share the same centre*

Figure 8.6 shows a simple electromagnet.

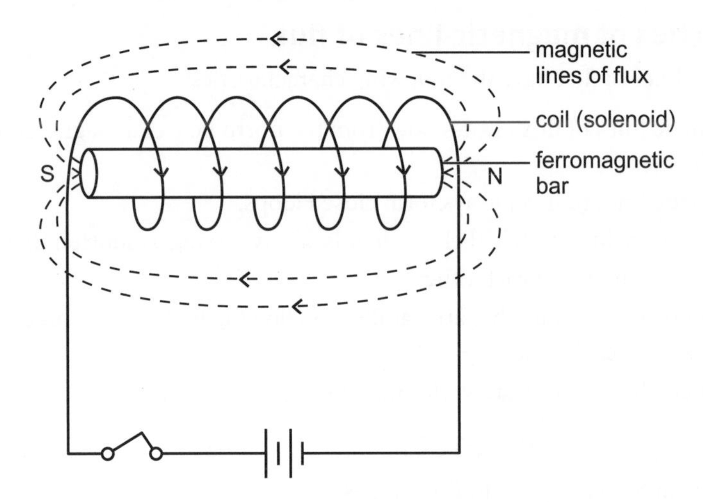

Figure 8.6: A simple electromagnet

The magnet is made up of a coil of closely spaced conductive wire, such as copper, that is wrapped around a ferromagnetic ***core***. When the electricity is switched on, current flows through the wire, also known as a ***solenoid***, creating a magnetic field and magnetising the core as if it were a permanent magnet.

Electromagnets are used as components in many electrical devices, including motors, generators and transformers, as well as in industry to lift and move heavy metallic objects such as cars or scrap metal.

8.1.3 Magnetic effects of electric currents

When electric current flows through any conductor, a magnetic field is produced around the entire length of the conductor. This magnetic field takes the form of ***concentric circles***.

Magnetic effects of electric currents on a conductor

Magnetic lines of flux are vector quantities. This means that they have magnitude and direction. Remember that magnetic lines of flux always flow from the north pole to the south pole of all magnets.

We will look at how to determine the direction of the magnetic lines of flux around:

- A current-carrying conductor.
- A current-carrying coil.

Direction of magnetic lines of flux around a current-carrying conductor

The direction of the magnetic field around any current-carrying conductor can be determined by the right-hand rule or the screw rule.

The right-hand rule

This rule states that if you hold a conductor in your right hand with your thumb pointing in the direction of the flow of current, the fingers curled around the conductor will point in the direction of the magnetic field.

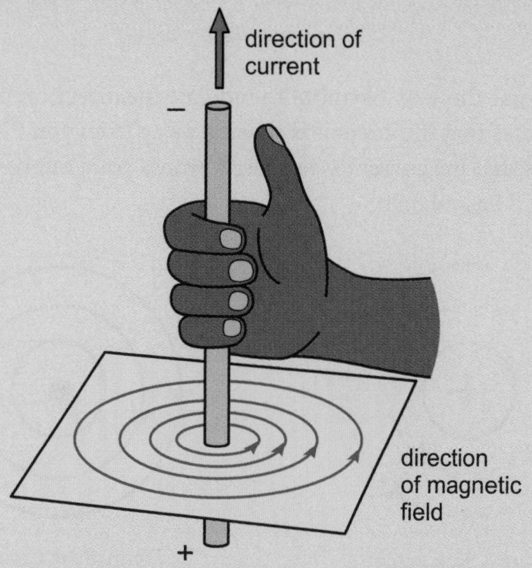

Figure 8.7: Finding the direction of magnetic field around a current-carrying conductor using the right-hand rule

The screw rule

Another method of determining the direction of the magnetic field around a current-carrying conductor is to use the screw rule.

This rule states that the direction of travel of a screw represents the direction of current flow and the direction of rotation of the screw represents the direction of the magnetic flux.

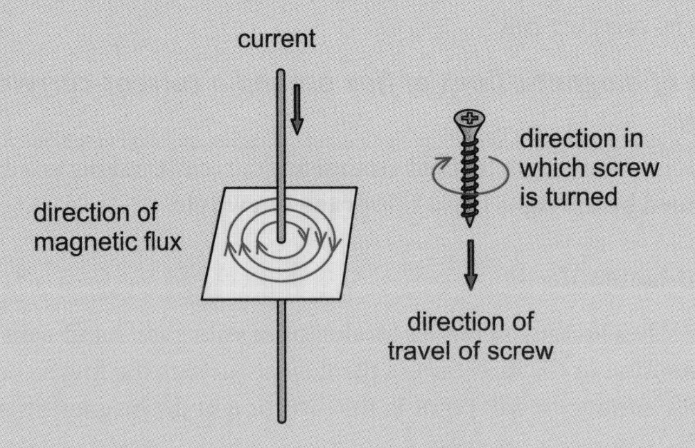

Figure 8.8: Finding the direction of magnetic field around a current-carrying conductor using the screw rule

In diagrams, we use the + or • symbol to indicate the direction in which current flows. A + indicates that the current is flowing away from you ('into the page'), and a • indicates that the current is flowing towards you ('out of the page'), as shown in Figure 8.9a and 8.9b.

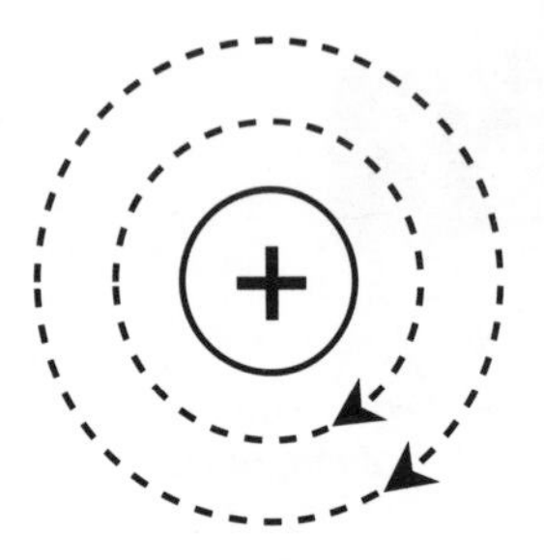

Figure 8.9a: Current flowing away from you; the + symbol (like the feather end of an arrow) means 'into the page'

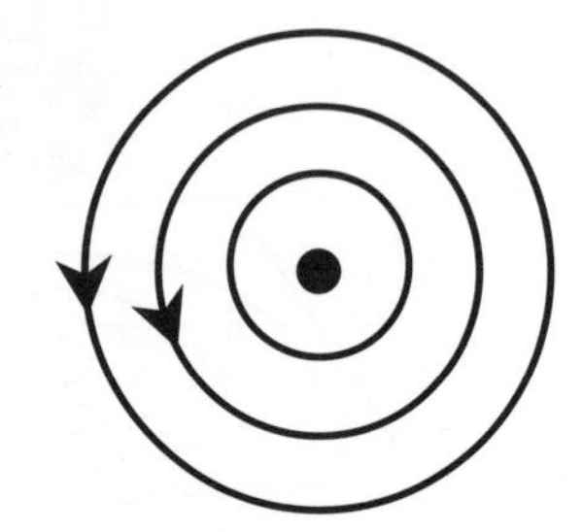

Figure 8.9b: Current flowing towards you; the • symbol (like the point of an arrow) means 'out of the page'

Magnetic effects of electric currents on a coil

Coils are used to concentrate magnetic lines of flux over a smaller area. When a coil or solenoid is ***excited*** or energised, it means a current is passing through

excited (coil): *supplied with current in order to convert it into an electromagnet; also called energised*

the solenoid, producing a magnetic flux and converting the coil into an electromagnet.

The strength of the magnetic field around a solenoid may be increased by:

- Increasing the number of turns in the coil.
- Increasing the current through the coil.
- Using thicker wire. (This is because a thicker wire has less resistance, so that more current can flow.)
- Inserting an iron core into the coil.

Direction of magnetic lines of flux around a current-carrying coil

Remember that magnetic lines of flux always flow from the north pole of a magnet to its south pole. To determine the north pole of an electromagnet, we use the right-hand grip rule.

Right-hand grip rule for a coil

This rule states that if you hold the coil in your right hand with your fingers pointing in the direction of the current, your outstretched thumb will point in the direction of the north pole of the electromagnet.

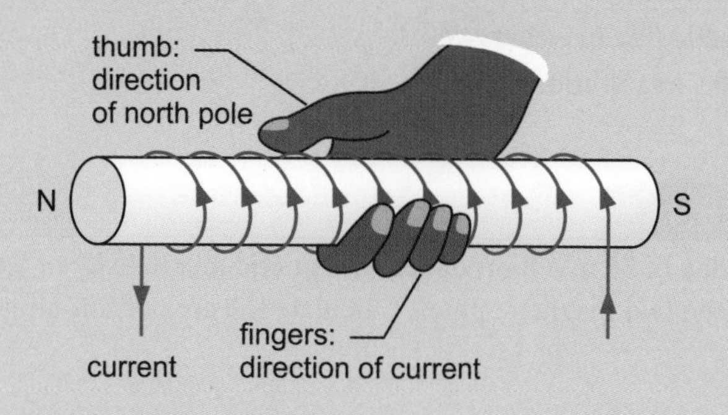

Figure 8.10: Direction of the north pole of an electromagnet

8.1.4 Magnetic flux density

Definition of magnetic flux density

Magnetic flux density is the amount of magnetic flux (ϕ) passing through a specific area.

Magnetic flux density is represented by the symbol B and is measured in teslas (T).

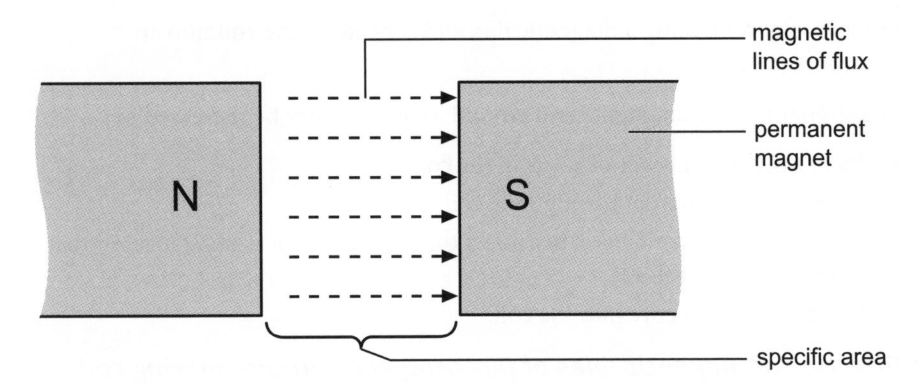

Figure 8.11: Magnetic flux density

Formula for calculating magnetic flux density

Magnetic flux density can be calculated using the formula:

$$B = \frac{\phi}{a}$$

where:

- B = magnetic flux density in teslas (T).
- ϕ = magnetic flux in webers (Wb).
- a = specific area in square metres (m^2).

Note

You will not be asked to calculate magnetic flux density in your exams at N1 level, however, it is an important concept for you to understand as groundwork for later levels.

Example 8.1

A magnetic flux of 36 mWb produces a magnetic flux density of 0,85 T in the air gap between two magnetic poles. Calculate the area of this air gap.

Solution

Given:

$\phi = 36$ mWb $\quad\quad B = 0{,}85$ T

$$B = \frac{\phi}{a}$$

$$a = \frac{\phi}{B}$$

$$= \frac{36 \times 10^{-3}}{0{,}85}$$

$$= 0{,}042 \text{ m}^2$$

8.1.5 Force (F) on a conductor inside a magnetic field

Definition of force

Force is a push or pull on an object with mass that causes it to change velocity.

Note

It is very important to understand how a force is produced on a current-carrying conductor inside a magnetic field. It is not listed as a learning outcome in the curriculum, but it is a critical concept to understand as groundwork (pre-knowledge) for N2 work and later levels.

Force is represented by the symbol F and is measured in newtons (N).

Force is a vector quantity, which means that it has both magnitude and direction.

Let us look at how a force is produced on a current-carrying conductor when it is placed inside a magnetic field:

1. Place two bar magnets next to each other. Although there is a magnetic field around each magnet, for our purpose we will focus only on the magnetic lines of flux spread over the area shown in Figure 8.12a.

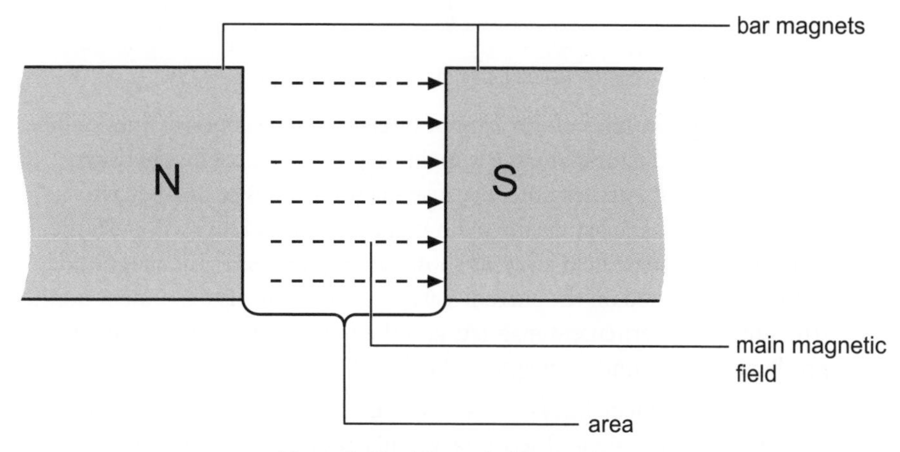

Figure 8.12a: Magnetic flux density

2. Let us ignore the magnetic fields around these two magnets. Now place a current-carrying conductor between these two magnets. (See Figure 8.12b.)

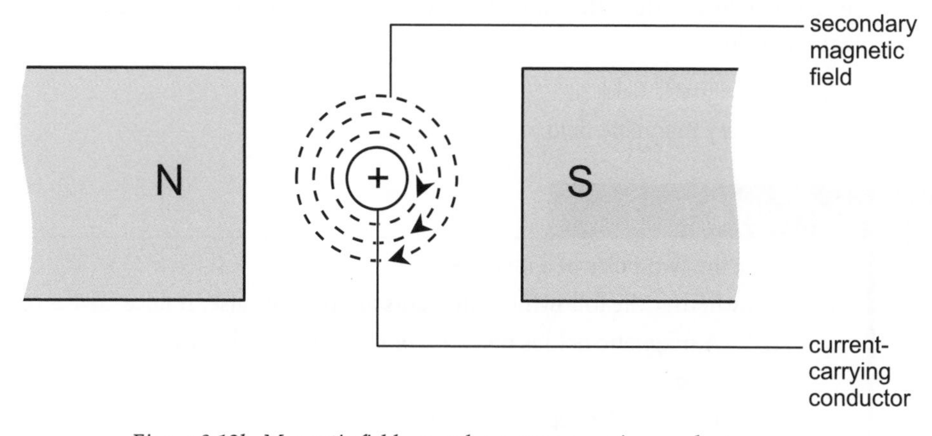

Figure 8.12b: Magnetic field around a current-carrying conductor

Note that the conductor is standing vertically, and the current is flowing away from you. The direction of the magnetic field is clockwise (using the right-hand rule).

3. Now merge the two diagrams. For future explanations, we will refer to the magnetic field produced by the magnets as the *main magnetic field* and that of the current-carrying conductor as the *secondary magnetic field.*

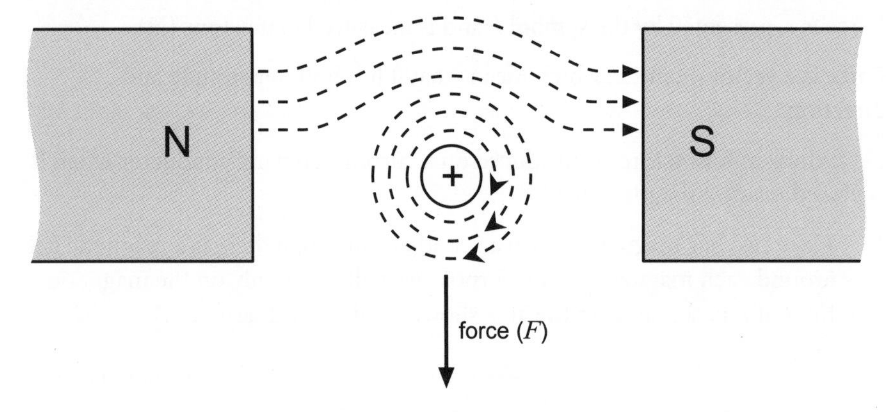

Figure 8.12c: Force exerted on conductor

4. Because magnetic lines of flux cannot intersect, the secondary lines of flux around the conductor ***distorts*** the main magnetic lines of flux between the bar magnets. Furthermore, because magnetic lines of flux behave like stretched elastic bands, the main magnetic lines of flux will push the secondary magnetic field away, as shown in Figure 1.65c. The magnitude of the force exerted on the current-carrying conductor is dependent on the strength of the permanent magnets and the magnitude of the current that is producing the secondary magnetic field.

   Because the magnetic lines of flux above the conductor are in the same direction for the main and secondary fields, they add together to form a stronger field. Below the conductor, they oppose each other, causing a weaker field. The stronger field above overcomes the weaker field below, resulting in a *downward* force, as shown in Figure 8.12c.

distort: *change the shape of something*

See it online

Force on a conductor in a magnetic field
What happens to a conductor in a magnetic field? Basic operating principle of a motor by Joe Robinson training | https://youtu.be/_f_WoDQu2Ag

We can therefore deduce that, for a force to be produced there must be two magnetic fields:

- A main magnetic field.
- A secondary magnetic field.

Activity 8.1

1. Name the two poles of a magnet. (2)
2. State whether the following statements are true or false. If false, give a reason.
   2.1 A magnetic field is made up of magnetic field lines.
   2.2 Like poles attract each other.
   2.3 Unlike poles repel each other.
   2.4 The magnetic field around any magnet is the weakest at the poles.
   2.5 Natural magnets are mined out of the earth. (8)
3. What do you understand by the term 'permanent magnet'? (3)
4. List three materials from which permanent magnets are made. (3)
5. What is an electromagnet? (3)

6.	State four uses of electromagnets.	(4)
7.	Make a neat, fully labelled sketch to show the magnetic field around a permanent magnet.	(4)
8.	What is the purpose of the right-hand grip rule?	(2)
9.	State the right-hand grip rule.	(3)
10.	What does exciting or energising a coil mean?	(3)
11.	State four methods that can be used to increase the strength of the magnetic field around a solenoid.	(4)
12.	State the right-hand rule.	(3)
13.	State the screw rule.	(3)
		TOTAL: [45]

Unit 8.2: Electromagnetism

electromagnetic: *concerning the relationship between electric currents and magnetic fields*

Definition of electromagnetism

Electromagnetism is the study of ***electromagnetic*** forces.

All domestic and industrial consumers are supplied with alternating currents. These currents reverse their direction of flow many times per second and at regular intervals. Let us try to understand this statement by carefully comparing a typical direct-current (DC) circuit to an alternating current (AC) circuit.

8.2.1 Direct-current circuit

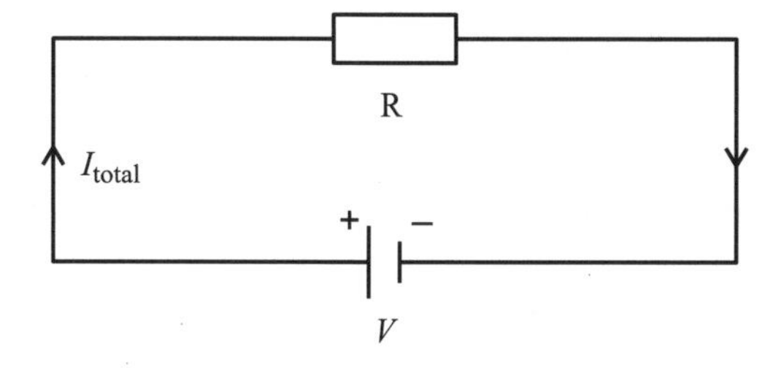

Figure 8.13: A simple DC circuit

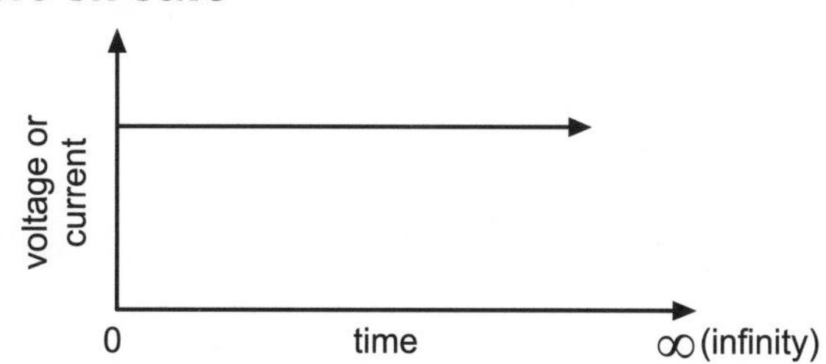

Figure 8.14: DC voltage or current waveforms

In any DC circuit, the movement of electrons or the flow of current is in one direction only. Conventional current flow is the flow of current from the positive terminal of a battery to the negative terminal of the battery. Electron flow is the flow of current from the negative terminal of a battery to the positive terminal of the battery.

Note that during the flow of this current, it experiences the resistance of resistor R. The voltage and current quantities can be represented by waveforms in the form of straight lines.

infinity (∞): *larger than any number*

Figure 8.14 shows that the voltage and current values are constant at any time from zero (0) to ***infinity*** (∞).

8.2.2 Alternating current circuit

Figure 8.15 shows a simple AC circuit. Note that the supply has no polarity, so we cannot determine the direction of current flow. Let us use the ***analogy*** of a simple piston and wheel system to explain alternating currents.

analogy: *a comparison between two things for the purpose of explanation*

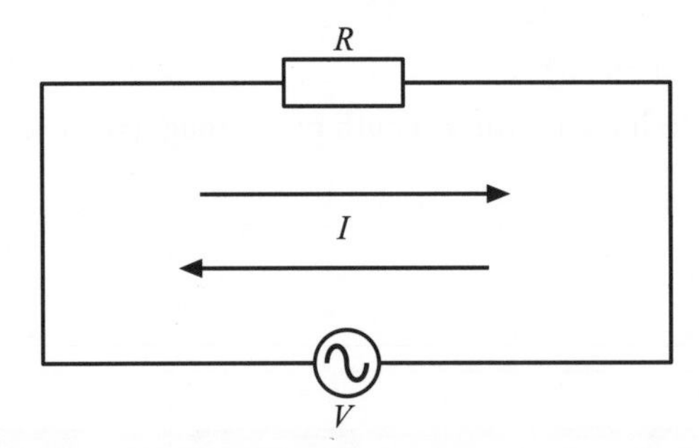

Figure 8.15: A simple AC circuit

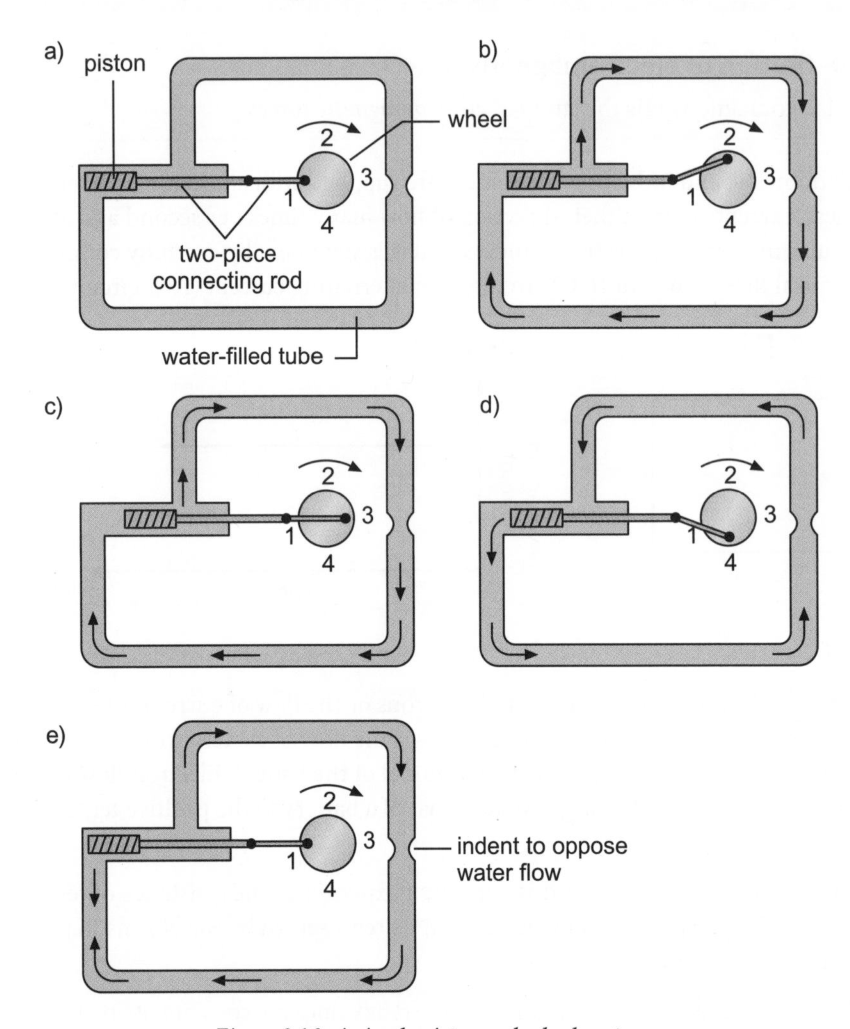

Figure 8.16: A simple piston and wheel system

As the wheel in Figure 8.16 turns in a clockwise direction from position 1 to position 3, the piston gradually moves from left to right. The movement of the piston displaces the water, causing the water to flow through the pipe system in a clockwise direction. The volume of water that is displaced by the piston gradually increases from zero to maximum displacement.

As the wheel further rotates from position 3 back to position 1, the piston gradually moves from right to left and the direction of the water through the pipe system is now in an anticlockwise direction. Again, the volume of water that is displaced gradually increases from zero to maximum displacement.

The indent in the pipe system restricts the flow of water (opposes water flow). This is similar to resistance in an electrical circuit. Now let us use this example to explain AC circuit theory.

The generation of an AC wave is best explained by Faraday's laws of electromagnetic induction.

8.2.3 Faraday's laws of electromagnetic induction

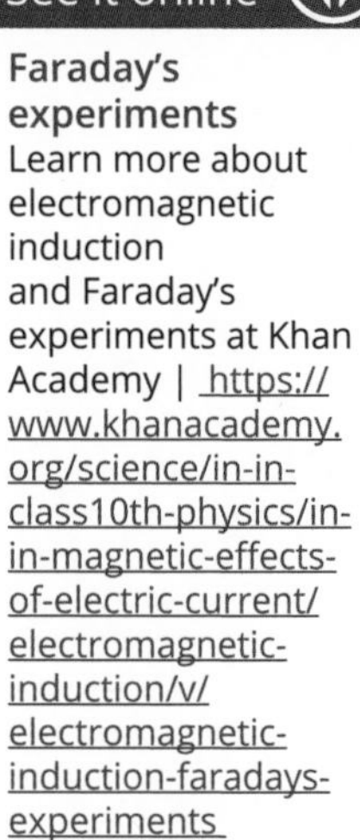

See it online

Faraday's experiments
Learn more about electromagnetic induction and Faraday's experiments at Khan Academy | https://www.khanacademy.org/science/in-in-class10th-physics/in-in-magnetic-effects-of-electric-current/electromagnetic-induction/v/electromagnetic-induction-faradays-experiments

Definition of electromagnetic induction

Electromagnetic induction is the process of producing an electromotive force across a coil linked to a changing magnetic field.

Michael Faraday was an English physicist and chemist. In 1831, he formulated the two laws of electromagnetic induction.

Faraday's first law of electromagnetic induction

Faraday's first law of electromagnetic induction states that:

An electromotive force (emf) or open-circuit voltage is always induced in a coil whenever the magnetic flux linking with the coil changes.

Faraday's second law of electromagnetic induction

Faraday's second law of electromagnetic induction states that:

*The magnitude of the induced emf is dependent on the rate of change of **flux linkages**.*

flux linkages: *the linking of a magnetic field with the conductors of a coil when the magnetic field passes through the loops of the coil*

Requirements for electromagnetic induction

Michael Faraday was able to prove that for an emf to be induced, three things are required:

- Magnetic lines of flux.
- A coil or conductor.
- Motion.

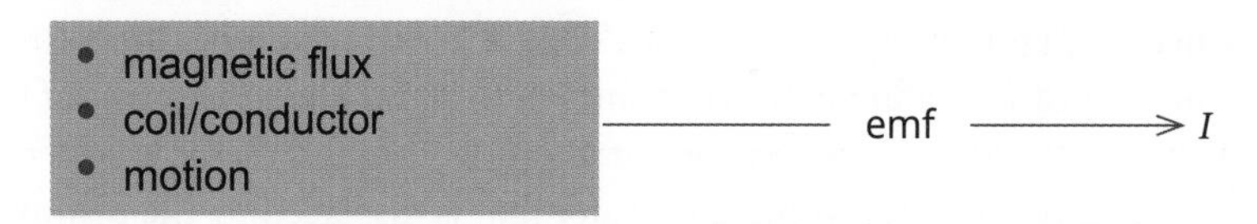

Figure 8.17: Diagrammatic representation of Faraday's first law

8.2.4 Types of electromagnetic induction

Emf can be induced in two ways, depending on the type of motion involved:

- Dynamically.
- Statically.

Dynamically induced emf

Faraday's laws can be simplified to read as follows:

When a conductor or coil moves or cuts across magnetic flux, an emf is induced in the coil or conductor. The magnitude of the emf is dependent on the rate of cutting.

dynamically induced emf: *emf that is produced as a result of physical motion*

If a wire coil is physically rotated inside a magnetic field, it causes an emf to be induced in the rotating coil. The emf is said to be ***dynamically induced***.

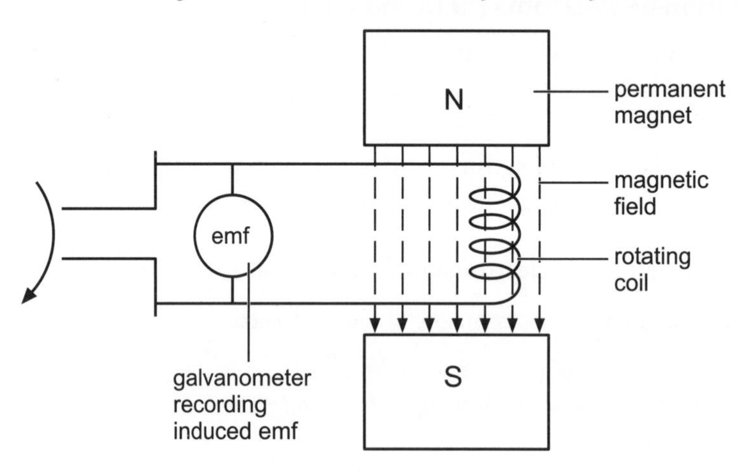

Figure 8.18: Dynamically induced emf

The motion in this case is the physical rotation of the coil, which we will be able to see.

Dynamically induced emf

When a coil is rotated inside a magnetic field, an emf is induced. This will in turn produce current flow if the circuit is closed.

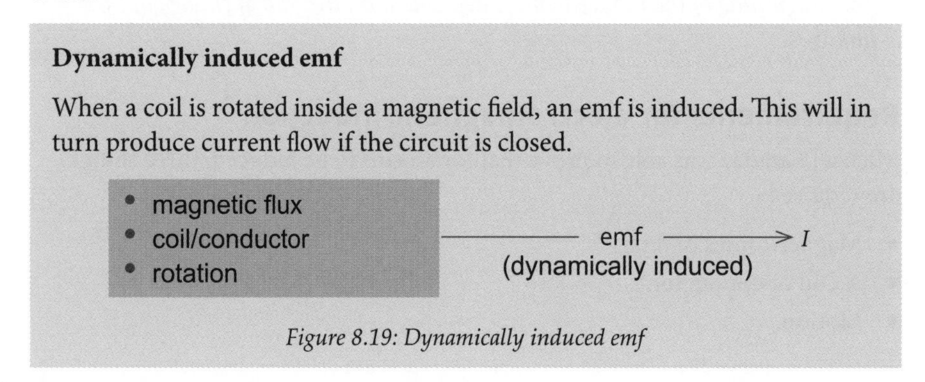

Figure 8.19: Dynamically induced emf

Statically induced emf

statically induced emf: *no physical motion is required to induce an emf; emf is induced by a changing magnetic field*

links: *associates*

oppose: *to resist change*

self-inductance: *the property of an electric circuit or coil that causes an emf to be generated within itself as a result of a changing current*

Statically induced emf

An emf is said to be ***statically induced*** when no physical motion is needed to induce an emf in a coil or conductor, but the magnetic field around the conductor changes instead.

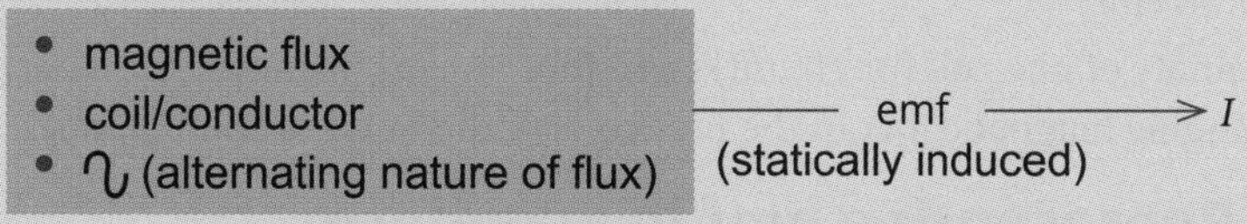

- magnetic flux
- coil/conductor
- ∿ (alternating nature of flux)

→ emf (statically induced) → I

Figure 8.20: Statically induced emf

In this way, the three requirements for electromagnetic induction are still present to induce the emf.

There are two types of statically induced emf, namely:

- Self-induced emf.
- Mutually induced emf.

Self-induced emf

- When a changing or alternating magnetic flux ***links*** with a coil, the alternating magnetic lines of flux will cut across the conductor of the coil and induce an emf in the coil.
- This emf will produce a current that will ***oppose*** the change of flux responsible for inducing it.
- The property of any coil that enables it to oppose such change (an increase or a decrease) in flux is known as ***self-inductance***. Inductance opposes current changes (we will discuss this further in N2).

Mutually induced emf

Faraday's experiment is shown in Figure 8.21.

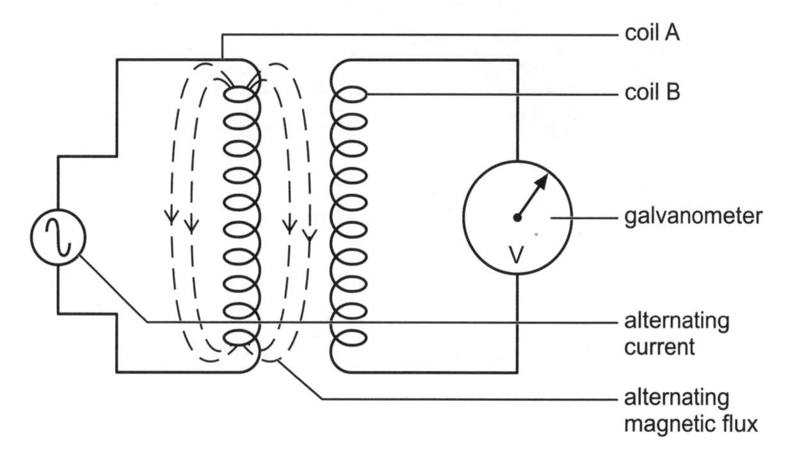

Figure 8.21: Mutually induced emf

- He used two coils. Coil A was connected to an alternating current supply, which in turn produced an alternating magnetic field. Coil B was connected to a galvanometer.
- As coil B was brought closer to coil A, the needle of the galvanometer began to deflect, indicating that an emf was being induced in the coil.
- This method of inducing an emf using two coils is referred to as mutually induced emf.
- The ability of one coil (or circuit) to induce an emf in another coil because of a changing magnetic flux in the first coil is called ***mutual inductance***.

mutual inductance: *ability of one coil (or circuit) to induce an emf in another coil because of a changing magnetic flux in the first coil*

alternator: *an electric generator that converts mechanical energy into electrical energy in the form of alternating currents*

8.2.5 Representing emf in waveform

Emf induced either dynamically or statically can be represented by a sinusoidal waveform. This waveform is also called a changing or alternating waveform.

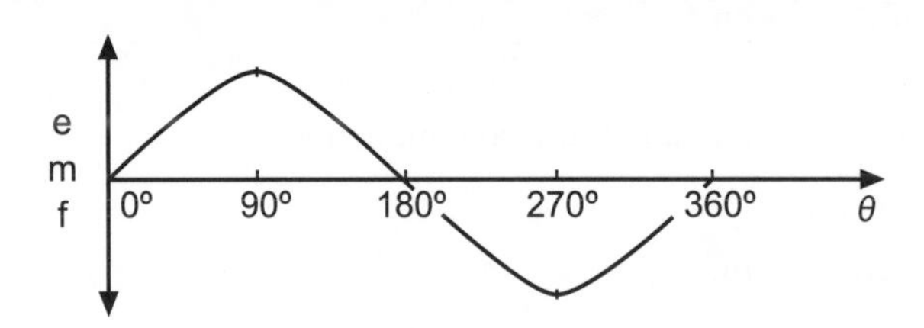

Figure 8.22: A sinusoidal waveform

See it online

Generating an AC waveform
Learn more about how an AC wave is generated in this video – AC Generator by Creative learning | https://youtu.be/gQyamjPrw-U

Let us now take a closer look at how this waveform is generated. Figure 8.23 shows a simple single-phase generator (***alternator***).

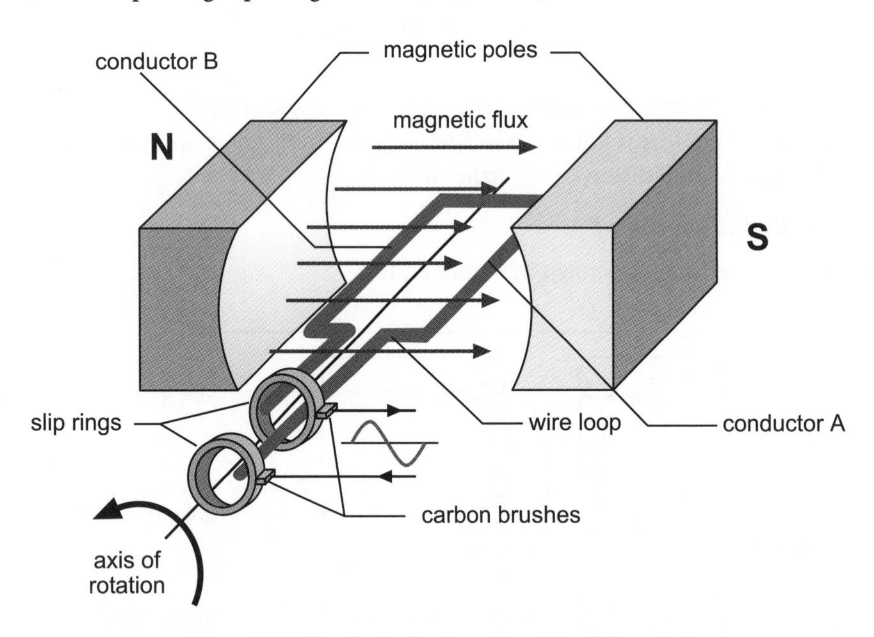

Figure 8.23: Simple single-phase generator (alternator)

Consider one conductor (conductor A) of the wire loop. In Figure 8.24 we are looking directly into the alternator and conductor A is pointing into the page.

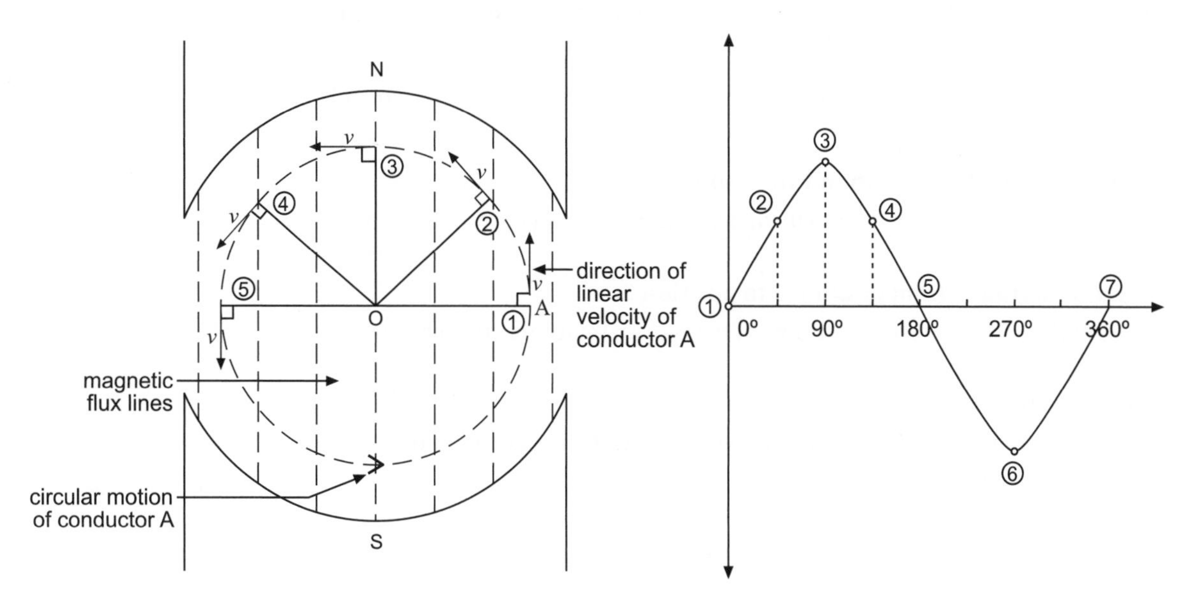

Figure 8.24: Generating an AC wave

We are interested in the motion (velocity) of the conductor relative to the magnetic lines of flux. Conductor A is moving on a circular path. At each instant it has a linear velocity (v) which is a vector quantity with magnitude and direction. This linear velocity is at a tangent to the circular path of the conductor. Note that at each instant, the direction of the velocity (v) changes.

- **Position 1:** When the conductor is at position 1, its direction of motion (velocity) does not cut any lines of flux because it is parallel to the lines of flux. No emf is induced.
- **Position 2:** As the conductor leaves position 1 and moves towards position 2, the direction of motion (velocity) begins to cut through the lines of flux. An emf is induced.
- **Position 3:** At position 3, the direction of motion (velocity) of the conductor is perpendicular to the magnetic lines of flux. This means that maximum lines of flux will be cut and maximum emf will be induced.
- **Position 4:** At position 4, which is similar to position 2, fewer lines of flux are cut. The emf is now reduced.
- **Position 5:** After 180° of rotation, the direction of motion (velocity) is again parallel to the lines of flux and no cutting takes place, so the induced emf is zero once again.

Up to the 180° point, we have completed the positive half cycle of the graph. During this time, the current is flowing in one direction.

The same explanation can be given for rotation from 180° to 360°, or the negative half of the cycle. During the negative half cycle, the current flows in the opposite direction. This is because the direction of the motion of the conductor relative to the magnetic lines of flux is reversed.

The sinusoidal waveform in Figure 8.24 represents one complete cycle, which is made up of four sections:

- **First section – from position 1 to position 3:**
  The emf increases from zero to its maximum, producing current flow in one direction.
- **Second section – from position 3 to position 5:**
  The emf decreases from its maximum to zero, maintaining current flow in the same direction.
- **Third section – from position 5 to position 6:**
  The emf increases from zero to its maximum, producing current flow in the reverse direction.
- **Fourth section – from position 6 to position 7:**
  The emf decreases from its maximum to zero, maintaining current flow in the reverse direction.

Activity 8.2

1.	What is the difference between direct current and alternating current?	(3)
2.	State Faraday's laws of electromagnetic induction.	(5)
3.	State the requirements for an emf to be induced.	(3)
4.	Explain what the following terms mean:	
	4.1 Dynamically induced emf.	(2)
	4.2 Statically induced emf.	(2)
		TOTAL: [15]

Summary of Module 8

We have covered the following in this module. See if you have mastered each of these sections.

Unit 8.1 Magnetism

- The area or region around any magnet is called a magnetic field and is made up of magnetic lines of flux (or magnetic field lines).
- All magnets have two poles: a north pole and a south pole.
- Like poles repel each other and unlike poles attract each other.
- Natural magnets, referred to as lodestone, are pieces of magnetic or other magnetised minerals that are found buried near the surface of the earth.
- Permanent magnets are those metals which retain their magnetism permanently after the external magnetic field has been removed.
- Electromagnets are temporary in the sense that a magnetic field is produced by an electric current, but the magnetic field disappears as soon as the current is turned off.
- Magnetic lines of flux are vector quantities, which means that they have magnitude and direction.
- The direction of the magnetic field around any current-carrying conductor is determined by the right-hand rule or the screw rule.
- To determine the north pole of an electromagnet, we use the right-hand grip rule.

Unit 8.2 Electromagnetism

- In any DC circuit, the movement of electrons or the flow of current is in one direction only.
- Conventional current flow is the flow of current from the positive terminal of a battery to the negative terminal of the battery.
- Electron flow is the flow of current from the negative terminal of a battery to the positive terminal of the battery.
- Alternating currents reverse their direction of flow many times per second and at regular intervals.
- Michael Faraday formulated the two laws of electromagnetic induction.
- The emf induced in a rotating coil is said to be dynamically induced.
- An emf is said to be statically induced when no physical motion is needed to induce the emf, but the magnetic field around the conductor changes instead.
- There are two types of statically induced emf, namely self-induced and mutually induced.
- Emf induced either dynamically or statically can be represented by a sinusoidal waveform.
- This sinusoidal waveform is also called a changing or alternating waveform.

Summative assessment for Module 8

1. What is the area or region around any magnet called? (1)
2. State five properties of magnetic lines of flux. (5)
3. List the three types of magnets. (3)
4. What is lodestone? (2)
5. Magnetic lines of flux are vector quantities. What does this mean? (2)
6. Explain the following:
   - **6.1** Conventional flow of current. (2)
   - **6.2** Electron flow of current. (2)
7. Name two types of statically induced emf. (2)
8. Explain what is meant by mutual inductance. (4)
9. Give two other names for a sinusoidal waveform. (2)

TOTAL: [25]

Renewable energy

Module
9

Overview of Module 9

Energy sources such as coal and crude oil are limited and will eventually be used up. Burning them for fuel releases greenhouse gases into the air. Renewable energy sources cannot run out (e.g. energy from the sun) or they can be easily replaced (e.g. wood from trees). All over the world, countries are trying to minimise the emission of greenhouse gases and use more renewable energy sources. This is important, because non-renewable energy sources and greenhouses gases are contributing to climate change.

In this module we are going to learn about the causes of climate change and the benefits of using renewable energy.

When you have completed this module, you should be able to:

Unit 9.1: Renewable energy, greenhouse gases and climate change

- Define renewable energy.
- Identify renewable energy sources.
- Explain the following terms:
  - Climate change, fossil fuel, greenhouse gases.
- State the benefits of using renewable energy.

Figure 9.1: Wind and solar energy are both forms of renewable energy sources

Starter activity

Discuss the following in class:

- Certain fruit and vegetables have to be cultivated in greenhouses because bad weather conditions may negatively affect their quality. What is your understanding of a greenhouse?
- The severe drought and high temperatures experienced in our country are attributed to global warming. What is global warming and what are its causes?
- Many countries throughout the world are moving towards renewable energy. What is renewable energy?

Unit 9.1: Renewable energy, greenhouse gases and climate change

9.1.1 How electricity is generated

Electricity is generated in power stations by large alternators, which are driven by ***prime movers***. These prime movers could be internal combustion engines, windmills or ***turbines***.

In Figure 9.2 we see the three requirements for inducing an emf (see Module 8, section 8.2.3). Rotation, the third requirement, is the function of the prime mover.

prime mover: *a natural or mechanical source of angular motion*

turbine: *a rotary mechanical device*

thermal: *relating to heat*

Figure 9.2: Pictorial representation of Faraday's law

The alternator's function is to convert mechanical energy into electrical energy, which is then supplied to the national electricity grid and ultimately to homes and businesses. Remember that the law of conservation of energy states that energy cannot be created and cannot be destroyed, it can only be converted from one form into another.

The prime mover will provide the mechanical energy after it has first converted some other form of energy into mechanical energy.

Coal-fired power stations

The most popular type of power station in South Africa is the coal-fired power station. In this ***thermal*** power station, coal is burned in a boiler and the heat energy that is produced is used to boil water. The boiling water produces steam and this steam is then passed through a nozzle where it is pressurised. The pressurised steam is passed through a turbine. When the steam hits the turbine blades, it sets the turbine into motion. The energy of the pressurised steam is converted into mechanical energy (rotation of the turbine) which is then turned into electricity by the alternator.

Figure 9.3: The Tutuka coal-fired power station in Mpumalanga, South Africa

Figure 9.4: Steam turbines are used in a coal-fired power station to drive the alternators

9.1.2 Renewable energy

greenhouse gases: *gases which have the ability to absorb* ***infrared radiation*** *(infrared light) emitted from the earth's surface and to radiate it back to the earth's surface*

infrared radiation: *electromagnetic radiation that is invisible to the human eye but can be felt as heat; also called infrared light*

deplete: *reduce*

replenish: *to fill up or make complete again*

finite: *limited quantity*

decomposed: *broken down*

dirty energy: *energy that is produced through means that pollute the atmosphere*

pollution: *the presence or introduction of a harmful or poisonous substance into the environment*

atmosphere: *gases surrounding the earth*

For the time being, coal is still found in abundance in our country. Unfortunately burning coal produces ***greenhouse gases*** which are harmful to the environment. (Greenhouse gases will be discussed in section 9.1.3).

Because of these harmful effects, efforts are being made all over the world to make greater use of renewable energy sources to produce electricity. Generating energy from renewable sources is kinder to our environment than generating energy from non-renewable sources such as coal.

What is renewable energy?

Definition of renewable energy

Renewable energy is energy that is produced by renewable resources which can be used repeatedly (they are not ***depleted***) or are ***replenished*** naturally.

Non-renewable energy

Non-renewable energy comes from sources that are ***finite***. The major sources of non-renewable energy are fossil fuels.

Definition of fossil fuels

Fossil fuels are natural energy sources (fuels) that formed in the earth over a very long period of time from the remains of ancient ***decomposed*** life forms (plants and animals).

The three most important fossil fuels are:

- Coal.
- Petroleum.
- Natural gas.

These sources of energy are available only in limited quantities and take an extremely long time to be replenished. Fossil fuels are also found only in certain parts of the world.

Non-renewable energy is also regarded as ***'dirty' energy*** because its use creates ***pollution*** in the ***atmosphere***. This contributes to climate change through the production of greenhouse gases.

Figure 9.5: Non-renewable and renewable energy sources

Renewable energy
Learn more in this video – Renewable Energy 101 by National Geographic | https://youtu.be/1kUE0BZtTRc

Types of renewable energy

Renewable energy is sometimes called ***clean energy***. Table 9.1 shows some of the common types of renewable energy and how they are used to create clean energy.

Table 9.1: Types of renewable energy

Renewable energy	Method of operation
Solar	In a solar power station large areas are covered with ***photovoltaic*** cells (solar cells). These solar cells convert sunlight directly into electricity.
Wind	Wind power is converted into mechanical power by means of a wind turbine.
Water	Turbines are used to convert the ***potential energy*** of falling water or the ***kinetic energy*** of fast flowing water into mechanical energy.
Geothermal	***Geothermal*** energy is the heat that comes from the rocks and fluids found beneath the earth's crust. This heat energy is used to produce steam to drive a steam turbine.
Biomass	***Biomass*** (purposely grown crops, wood, animal or human waste) is burned in a furnace and the heat energy is used to produce steam to drive a steam turbine.
Ocean	A wave energy converter (WEC) converts the kinetic and potential energy of ocean waves into mechanical energy. This mechanical energy is used to drive a turbine.
Hydrogen	This method of generating electricity uses ***fuel cells***. A fuel cell converts chemical energy into electrical energy. The chemical energy is the result of a chemical reaction of hydrogen (fuel) and oxygen (oxidising agent).

Benefits of renewable energy

We have seen that renewable energy is much friendlier to the environment than non-renewable energy. It does not produce greenhouse gases (see section 9.1.3). It also has many other advantages:

- A safe and a clean form of energy.
- Cannot run out.
- Available in abundance.
- Provides the foundation for energy independence.
- Has many health and environmental benefits.
- Very economical.
- Resources are not restricted to certain parts of the world only.
- There are multiple forms of renewable energy.

clean energy: *energy that is produced through means that do not pollute the atmosphere*

photovoltaic: *able to produce electricity from light*

potential energy: *energy possessed by a body because of its position relative to another body*

kinetic energy: *energy possessed by a body because of its motion*

geothermal: *produced by the internal heat of the earth*

biomass: *organic matter used as fuel*

fuel cell: *cell in which hydrogen-rich fuel is converted into clean electricity through a chemical reaction*

9.1.3 Greenhouse gases and climate change

Greenhouse gases that are produced by non-renewable energy sources are harmful to the environment and contribute to climate change.

What are greenhouse gases?

Definition of greenhouse gases

Greenhouse gases are gases which have the ability to absorb infrared radiation (infrared light) emitted from the earth's surface and to radiate it back to the earth's surface.

Infrared radiation, also called infrared light, is invisible to the human eye but its heat can be felt.

greenhouse effect: *a process that occurs when gases in the earth's atmosphere trap the sun's heat*

Greenhouse gases make up only a fraction of all atmospheric gases but they have a huge impact on the energy levels of this planet. They also greatly contribute to climate change through what is known as the ***greenhouse effect***.

The most important greenhouse gases are:

- Carbon dioxide.
- Methane.
- Water vapour.

The greenhouse effect

See it online

The greenhouse effect
Learn more in this video – What is the greenhouse effect? by DW News | https://youtu.be/BPJJM_hCFj0

A greenhouse (also called a glasshouse or a hothouse) is a room where the walls and roof are made of transparent materials. These greenhouses are used to grow plants that need warmth and protection.

Sunlight penetrates the transparent outer shell and heats the air inside the room. Any heat that is not absorbed by the plants is trapped by the enclosure.

Figure 9.6: A typical greenhouse

The earth, sun and the atmosphere work on the same principle, but on a much larger scale and with a different physical process.

Sunlight penetrates the earth's atmosphere and heats the surface of the earth. Some of the sun's energy is reflected directly back to space and the rest is absorbed by land, the ocean and the atmosphere. The greenhouse gases that form part of the atmosphere trap the heat energy radiating from the earth towards space. This is known as the 'greenhouse effect'.

The greenhouse gases trap enough heat to support the energy needs of life on the planet. In the absence of these gases, the planet would not have enough heat to sustain life.

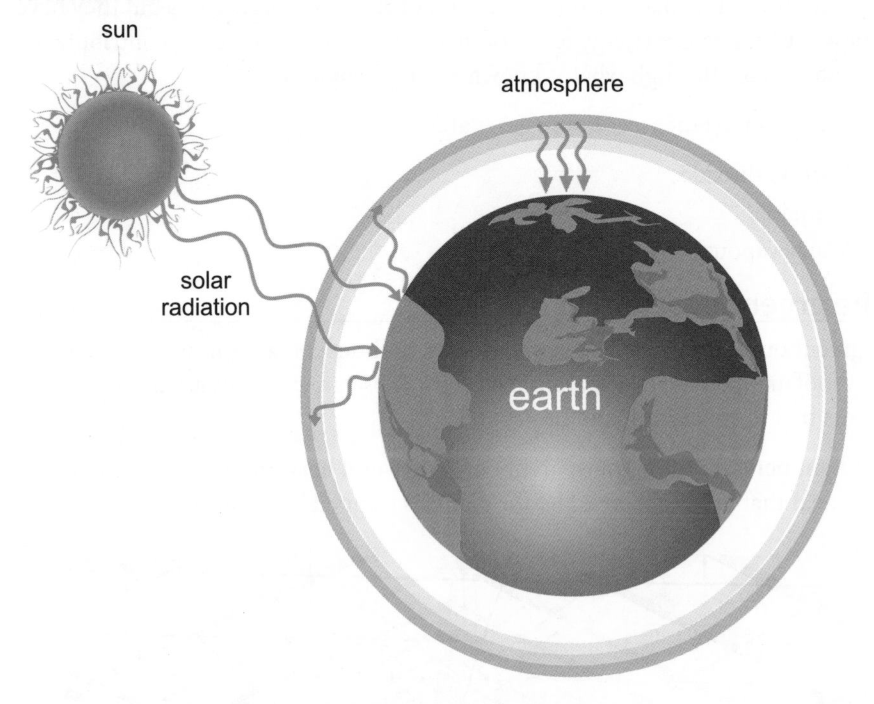

Figure 9.7: The greenhouse effect

So what is the big deal about greenhouse gases?

The problem is the increased level of greenhouse gases in the atmosphere caused by human activity. This increased level of greenhouse gases traps *too much* solar energy and radiates it back towards the surface of the earth. This upsets the natural systems that are responsible for regulating our climate.

Climate change

Definition of climate

The climate is the usual condition of the temperature, humidity, atmospheric pressure, wind, rainfall, etc. in an area of the earth's surface for a long period of time.

Definition of climate change

Climate change is any important long-term change in the expected patterns of the average weather of a region (or the whole planet) over a relatively long period of time.

Simply put, climate change is about *abnormal changes* in the climate.

Table 9.2 shows some of the direct and indirect consequences of climate change.

Table 9.2: Consquences of climate change

Direct consequences	Indirect consequences
• ***Global warming*** (i.e. rising minimum and maximum temperatures). • Warming oceans. • Shrinking ***glaciers*** (melting ice). • Rising sea levels. • Increased ***wildfires***. • Extreme weather patterns: ◦ Extreme heatwaves. ◦ Longer, more intense droughts. ◦ Increased flooding. ◦ ***Hurricanes*** becoming stronger and more intense.	• Health risks because of heatwaves and lack of clean water. • Hunger because of severe heat and extreme weather that destroy crops and other food sources. • Oceans swallowing land and the destruction of small islands. • Need for plants, animals and human beings to adapt. • Forced relocation of plants, animals and humans. • ***Extinction*** of plant and animal species. • Increase in ***pests*** and ***pathogens***.

global warming: *a gradual increase in the average temperature of the earth's atmosphere as a result of the greenhouse effect*

glacier: *a very large body of ice which moves very slowly*

wildfire: *large, destructive fire in a wild area such as a bush, forest or grassland*

hurricane: *large, rotating tropical storm with high winds and heavy rain*

extinction: *destroyed so that it no longer exists*

pest: *insect or small animal that damages crops or food supplies*

pathogen: *small organism, such as a virus, bacterium or fungus, that can cause disease*

fermentation: *chemical process in which a substance breaks down into a simpler substance*

rice paddy: *a field planted with rice growing in water*

Human activities that increase greenhouse gases

In addition to burning fossil fuels, other human activities can also contribute to climate change by either producing greenhouse gases or contributing to increasing their presence in the atmosphere. See Table 9.3.

Table 9.3: Human activities that increase greenhouse gases

Activity	Description
Burning fossil fuels	When fossil fuels (such as coal, petroleum and natural gas) are burned, they release carbon dioxide and other greenhouse gases into the atmosphere.
Deforestation	Cutting down trees contributes to climate change because trees absorb carbon dioxide.
Manufacture of cement	Carbon dioxide is emitted from the limestone that is used to manufacture cement.
Domesticated animals	***Fermentation*** of food in the digestive tracts of cattle, goats, sheep, pigs, etc. produces the greenhouse gas methane. Methane is also produced by the decomposition of animal manure.
Rice cultivation	Bacteria and other microorganisms that are found in the soil of flooded ***rice paddies*** decompose organic matter and this produces methane.
Garbage and human waste	The decomposition of garbage in landfill sites and the decomposition of human waste in sewage plants produce methane.

Using renewable energy to reduce the use of fossil fuels and reducing other activities listed in Table 9.3 are necessary to slow down climate change.

Activity 9.1

1. What is the function of a prime mover? (2)
2. List three types of prime movers that are used in the generation of electricity. (3)
3. List the three requirements to induce an emf. (3)
4. Which type of power station is the most popular in our country? (1)
5. List the three most important greenhouse gases. (3)
6. Why are increased levels of greenhouse gases undesirable? (4)
7. What is the function of a greenhouse? (3)
8. What purpose do greenhouse gases serve? (3)
9. What does climate change mean? (3)
10. List four human activities that contribute to greenhouse gas emission. (4)
11. List three types of fossil fuels. (3)
12. What is renewable energy? (3)
13. What are the consquences of climate change for a country like South Africa? (5)

TOTAL: [40]

Summary of Module 9

We have covered the following in this module. See if you have mastered each of these sections.

Unit 9.1 Renewable energy, greenhouse gases and climate change

- A prime mover is used to convert some other form of energy into mechanical energy.
- Prime movers could be internal combustion engines, windmills or turbines.
- The most popular type of power station in South Africa is the coal-fired power station.
- Coal is found in abundance in South Africa, but unfortunately burning coal produces greenhouse gases.
- Renewable energy is energy that is produced by renewable resources which could be used repeatedly and replenished naturally.
- Renewable energy sources do not produce greenhouse gases or contribute to climate change.
- Types of renewable energy include solar, wind, water, geothermal, biomass, ocean and hydrogen energy.
- The major sources of non-renewable energy are fossil fuels such as coal, petroleum and natural gas.
- Some of the sun's energy penetrating the earth's atmosphere is absorbed by land, the ocean and the atmosphere, while the balance is reflected back to space.
- Greenhouse gases have the ability to absorb infrared radiation (infrared light) emitted from the earth's surface and to radiate it back to the earth's surface (greenhouse effect).
- Carbon dioxide, methane and water vapour are the most important greenhouse gases.
- Greenhouse gases make up only a fraction of all atmospheric gases.

- Infrared radiation, also called infrared light, is invisible to the human eye but its heat can be felt.
- A greenhouse is a room where the walls and roof are made of transparent materials. It is designed to trap heat energy from sunlight.
- Human activity increases the levels of greenhouse gases in the atmosphere.
- Increased levels of greenhouse gases trap too much solar energy. This upsets the natural systems that are responsible for regulating our climate.
- The climate is the usual condition of the temperature, humidity, atmospheric pressure, wind, rainfall, etc. in an area of the earth's surface for a long period of time.
- Climate change is any important long-term change in the expected patterns of the average weather of a region (or the whole planet) over a relatively long period of time.
- Direct consequences of climate change include global warming, warming oceans, shrinking glaciers, increased wildfires and extreme weather patterns.
- Indirect consequences of climate change include risk to human health, starvation, forced relocation, extinction of plant and animal species and increases in pests and pathogens.

Summative assessment for Module 9

1. Why are coal-fired power stations very popular in our country? (1)
2. Why are coal-fired power stations undesirable? (1)
3. What is a greenhouse? (2)
4. What contributes to increased levels of greenhouse gases? (1)
5. What do you understand by climate? (3)
6. Why is non-renewable energy regarded as 'dirty' energy? (1)
7. What do you understand by renewable energy? (2)
8. List five types of renewable energy. (5)
9. State four advantages of renewable energy. (4)

TOTAL: [20]

Short answers

Module 4

Activity 4.1

12. 9,6 A
13. 19,167 Ω
14. 120 V

15.1 4 A
15.2 2 A
15.3 8 A

Activity 4.2

4.1 40 Ω
4.2 1 000 W
4.3 5,4 MJ

5.1 5 A
5.2 48 Ω
5.3 1,08 MJ

6.1 3 000 W
6.2 19,2 Ω
6.3 5,4 MJ

7.1 18 000 s
7.2 5,556 kW
7.3 23,15 A
7.4 10,367 Ω
7.5 R1 213,43
8. R122,85

Activity 4.3

4.1 65 Ω
4.2 3,385 A
4.3 3,385 A; 3,385 A;
4.4 84,625 V; 135,4 V
4.5 744,7 W

5.1 95 Ω
5.2 142,5 V

7.1 1,8 A
7.2 18,599 A

8.1 16,216 Ω
8.2 15,417 A
8.3 250 V; 250 V; 250 V
8.4 6,25 A; 5 A; 4,167 A
8.5 1 250 W
8.6 211,986 kJ

9.1 2,5 A
9.2 96 V
9.3 96 V; 96 V
9.4 38,4 Ω; 43,636 Ω

10. 10 Ω

Activity 4.4

1.1 20 Ω
1.2 24 Ω
1.3 44 Ω
1.4 84 V
1.5 154 V
1.6 2,1 A; 1,4 A; 3,5 A
1.7 117,6 W

2.1 35,172 Ω
2.2 6,824 A
2.3 2,824 A; 2,824 A; 4 A
2.4 141,2 V; 98,84 V; 240 V
2.5 245,678 kJ

3.1 50,909 Ω
3.2 3,929 A
3.3 1,429 A; 1,429 A; 2,5 A; 2,5 A
3.4 142,9 V; 57,16 V; 120 V; 80 V

Activity 4.5

4.1 375×10^{-3} m or 0,375 m
4.2 25×10^{3} m or 25 000 m
4.3 58×10^{-2} m or 0,58 m
4.4 120×10^{-4} m or 0,012 m^2
4.5 780×10^{-6} m^2 or 0,00078 m^2
4.6 $1,25 \times 10^{-6}$ Ωm

5. 2,765 Ω

6. 565,941 m

7. $3,984 \times 10^{-5}$ m^2

Activity 4.6

6. 11,02 Ω

7. 46,512 °C

8. 92,308 °C

Activity 4.7

7.1 12 V; 2,4 Ω
7.2 2 V; 0,067 Ω

8.1 30 Ω
8.2 8,8 V
8.3 1,6 Ω
8.4 0,278 A
8.5 0,445 V
8.6 8,34 V
8.7 3,336 V

9.1 2,1 V
9.2 0,4 Ω
9.3 9 Ω
9.4 0,223 A
9.5 0,089 V
9.6 2,011 V

Summative assessment for Module 4

8. 38,4 Ω

9. 10,667 A

10. 230 V

13.1 2 562 s
13.2 30 600 s
13.3 3,475 MJ
13.4 988,026 kJ

14.1 0,399 A
14.2 91,77 W
14.3 495,179 kJ

15.1 3,864 A
15.2 112,211 kJ
15.3 56,936 Ω

17.1 200 V
17.2 5,5 A
17.3 5,5 A; 5,5 A
17.4 4,95 MJ

18.1 8 Ω
18.2 12,5 A
18.3 100 V; 100 V; 100 V
18.4 5,556 A; 4,167 A; 2,778 A
18.5 555,644 W; 416,733 W; 277,822 W

19. 12 Ω

20.1 23,81 Ω
20.2 4,2 A
20.3 28 V; 72 V
20.4 2,8 A; 1,4 A; 2,4 A; 1,8 A
20.5 129,6 W
20.6 9 408 J

23. 11,05 Ω

24. $4,935 \times 10^{-3}$ m or 4,935 mm

26. 6,258 Ω

27. 88,384 °C

28.1 11,1 V; 6 Ω
28.2 1,85 V; 0,167 Ω

29.1 1,714 A
29.2 6,856 V
29.3 6,856 V

30.1 3,8 Ω
30.2 11,4 V

Abbreviations and symbols

α: alpha; temperature coefficient of resistance

α_θ: temperature coefficient of resistance at θ °C

α_0: temperature coefficient of resistance at 0 °C

Δt: change in temperature

μΩ: micro-ohm

μΩ m: micro-ohm metre

Ω: ohm

Ωm: ohm metre

π: pi

ρ: rho; resistivity in ohm metres (Ωm)

ϕ: magnetic flux in webers (Wb)

a: cross-sectional area in square metres (m^2); specific area in square metres (m^2)

A: ampere

AC: alternating current

B: magnetic flux density in teslas (T)

c: cent

C: coulomb

cm: centimetre

CoC: Certificate of Compliance

d: diameter of a conductor in metres (m)

dam: decametre

DC: direct current

dm: decimetre

E: emf in volts (V)

E_1: emf of one cell

E_{total}: total emf of a battery

ELR: earth leakage relay

emf: electromotive force

hm: hectometre

I: current in amperes (A)

$I_{//}$: current through parallel combination

I_1, I_2, I_3: currents 1, 2 and 3

I_{total}: total current drawn from the supply

IEC: International Electrotechnical Commission

J: joule

kJ: kilojoule

km: kilometre

kW: kilowatt

kWh: kilowatt-hour; units of energy consumed

l: length in metres (m)

LED: light-emitting diode

m: metre

mΩ: milli-ohm

MJ: megajoule

mm: millimetre

n: number of cells

nΩ: nano-ohm

NOSA: National Occupational Safety Association

OHS Act: Occupation Health and Safety Act 85 of 1993

pΩ: pico-ohm

P: power in watts (W)

P_{total}: total power in watts (W)

PD: potential difference

PPE: personal protective equipment

PVC: polyvinyl chloride

Q: heat energy in joules (J)

r: internal resistance in ohms (Ω); radius of conductor in metres (m)

r_1: internal resistance of one cell

r_{total}: total internal resistance of a battery

R: resistance in ohms (Ω); external resistance in ohms (Ω)

$R_{//}$: resistance of the parallel combination

R_{θ}: resistance at θ °C

R_0: resistance at 0 °C

$\mathrm{R_1}$, $\mathrm{R_2}$, $\mathrm{R_3}$: resistors 1, 2 and 3

R_1, R_2, R_3: resistance of resistors 1, 2 and 3

R_S: resistance of series path

R_t: resistance at temperature t

R_{total}: total resistance

s: second

SABS: South African Bureau of Standards

SANS: South African National Standards

SPD: surge protection device

t: time in seconds (s); temperature

V: volt

V: potential difference (terminal voltage) in volts (V); voltage drop in volts (V)

$V_{//}$: voltage drop across parallel combination

V_1, V_2, V_3: voltage drops 1, 2 and 3

V_{int}: internal voltage drop in volts (V)

V_{total}: total potential difference in volts (V)

W: watt

WEC: wave energy converter

x: tariff per unit of energy consumed

Glossary

abrasive: *rough or coarse 36*

accident: *an undesired and unplanned event that results in personal injury and/or damage to property and/or business interruption 4*

alloy: *a mixture of two or more metals 77*

alternating current (AC): *current that reverses its direction of flow many times per second 51*

alternator: *an electric generator that converts mechanical energy into electrical energy in the form of alternating currents 152*

ammeter: *an instrument for measuring electric current in amperes (A) 107*

ampere: *a unit of electric current equal to a flow of one coulomb per second, where the fixed numerical value of the elementary charge e is taken to be* $1{,}602176634 \times 10^{-19}$ *when expressed in coulomb 43*

analogy: *a comparison between two things for the purpose of explanation 148*

annealed: *heat treated to increase ductility and reduce hardness 100*

apparel: *covering for the human body; clothing 9*

arc shield: *protective welding helmet 17*

assembly point: *a location specified as the place for a group of people to gather in an emergency 26*

atmosphere: *gases surrounding the earth 159*

atom: *the smallest particle of an element 42*

bakelite: *a type of synthetic resin 101*

bar: *prevent or prohibit 13*

battery: *two or more identical cells connected together in series or in parallel 80*

bell tester: *a simple tester that sounds a bell when it detects continuity 129*

biomass: *organic matter used as fuel 160*

bonded: *electrically joined together 114*

bonding: *electrically joined together 130*

bridge: *to electrically connect two points 129*

burrs: *raised edges or small pieces of unwanted metal on a chisel 32*

busbar: *an electrical conductor, capable of carrying a high current, usually used to make a common connection between several circuits in a system 13*

capacitor: *an electronic device that stores electrical energy in an electric field 107*

cell: *a device that stores chemical energy and converts it into electrical energy 80*

Certificate of Compliance (CoC): *issued by a registered person in respect of an electrical installation or part of an electrical installation 128*

chuck: *a specialised clamp used to hold the rotating drill bit in position 36*

circuit: *a movement that starts and finishes at the same point 43*

circuit breaker: *a protective switch that automatically interrupts current flow in the event of an overload or short circuit; can be reset and reused 14*

clean energy: *energy that is produced through means that do not pollute the atmosphere 160*

climate: *the usual condition of the temperature, humidity, atmospheric pressure, wind, rainfall, etc. in an area of the earth's surface for a long period of time 162*

climate change: *any important long-term change in the expected patterns of the average weather of a region (or the whole planet) over a relative long period of time 162*

closed electric circuit: *a complete electrical connection around which current flows 43*

coefficient of thermal expansion: *describes the fractional change in the size of an object when its temperature changes 100*

coil: *a length of wire wound in a joined sequence of concentric rings (turns) 78*

combustible: *able to burn easily 23*

concentric: *having a common centre 78*

concentric circles: *two or more circles that share the same centre 140*

conductivity: *a property or characteristic that describes how well a material allows current to flow through it 96*

conductor: *any substance that allows electrons to move easily from one atom to another when a potential difference is applied across this substance 45, 96*

conduit box: *round PVC box with a lid in which conductor joints are made 105*

conventional current flow: *flow of current from the positive terminal of a battery to the negative terminal of the battery 43*

core: *a magnetic material with a high permeability used to confine and guide magnetic fields 140*

cross-sectional area: *area of the surface exposed by making a straight perpendicular slice through a three-dimensional object 71*

current: *the movement or flow of negative-charge carriers (electrons) in a specific direction 43*

current transformer: *instrument transformer used to step down currents to values that are safe to measure 107*

decomposed: *broken down 159*

dedicated socket outlet: *an outlet that supplies power to one device or appliance 116*

deplete: *reduce 159*

dielectric strength: *insulating strength 100*

diode: *a two-terminal semiconductor device that allows current to flow in one direction only 103*

direct current (DC): *electric current that flows in one direction only 41*

directly proportional: *the bigger one value, the bigger another value; for example, the bigger the voltage, the bigger the current (Ohm's law) 46*

dirty energy: *energy that is produced through means that pollute the atmosphere 159*

disconnector: *a switch used to open or break a circuit by disconnecting it from its energy supply during maintenance 12*

dissipate: *cause energy to be lost through its conversion into heat 41*

distort: *change the shape of something 146*

distribution board: *an enclosure that contains electrical equipment for the distribution or control of electrical power from one or more incoming circuits to one or more outgoing circuits 110*

distribution transformer: *transformer that ensures the final reduction (step down) of voltage before supplying consumers 108*

double-wound transformer: *transformer having two windings which are electrically isolated from each other 107*

drill quill: *the hollow shaft surrounding the spindle to which the chuck is mounted 36*

ductile: *can be drawn out into a thin wire 96*

dynamically induced emf: *emf that is produced as a result of physical motion 150*

earth: *to discharge electrical energy directly into the ground 13*

earth bar: *copper bar in the distribution board to which all earth continuity conductors and the earth lead are connected 110*

earth continuity conductor: *conductor, including any clamp or terminal, that connects the consumer's earth terminal (earth bar) to the exposed conductive parts of an installation 110*

earth leakage relay (ELR): *a protective device used to automatically disconnect an installation from the supply in the event of the leakage current exceeding a certain predetermined value 15*

earth leakage unit: *a device that is capable of detecting the flow of a specified or predetermined current from a circuit to earth, and of disconnecting, automatically and reliably, the affected circuit within a specified time when such current exceeds the specified or predetermined value 121*

earthing: *electrically connecting all points of consumption, switches and all exposed (conductive parts) of an installation to the general mass of the earth 121*

Edison-screw-type lamp: *standard lightbulb having a right-hand threaded metal base which screws into a matching threaded socket 116*

electric power tool: *a power tool that is powered by an electric motor that is supplied by either a battery (cordless power tool) or an electricity socket 34*

electrical load: *anything that requires current to operate 47*

electricity (current flow): *flow of charge (electrons) in a specific direction 43*

electrocute: *injure or kill by electric shock 12*

electrolyte: *a substance that separates into ions in solution and obtains the capacity to conduct electricity 77*

electromagnet: *a magnet created when current flows through a coil 139*

electromagnetic: *concerning the relationship between electric currents and magnetic fields 147*

electromagnetic induction: *the process of producing an electromotive force across a coil linked to a changing magnetic field 149*

electromagnetism: *the study of electromagnetic forces 147*

electromotive force (emf): *the voltage measured across the ends of an energy source of an open circuit 44*

electron: *negative-charge carrier 42*

electron flow: *the flow of current from the negative terminal of a battery to the positive terminal of the battery 43*

elementary charge: *charge carried by a single electron 43*

employee: *any person having a contract of employment or contract of training 3*

employer: *any person, company, partnership or non-profit organisation that employs one or more employees 3*

energy: *the capacity for doing work 50*

evacuation plan: *document or diagram or sign showing the safest emergency exit routes from a building 26*

excited (coil): *supplied with current in order to convert it into an electromagnet; also called energised 142*

extinction: *destroyed so that it no longer exists 163*

extinguish: *put an end to; put out 23*

fermentation: *chemical process in which a substance breaks down into a simpler substance 163*

ferromagnetism: *the mechanism by which certain metals, such as iron, nickel and cobalt, are magnetised by an external magnetic field and retain their magnetism after this field has been removed 139*

ferrule: *a copper or aluminium tube used to join conductors 31*

field coils: *insulated copper wire wound round the field poles of a DC motor or generator; also called field windings 79*

filament: *a conducting wire with a high melting point, forming part of an electric bulb that is made incandescent by passing an electric current through it 45*

finite: *limited quantity 159*

fire: *a process that occurs when a combustible material combines chemically with oxygen in the air and extreme heat, and gives off bright light, heat and smoke 23*

fire extinguisher: *a portable device that sprays water, foam, gas or other chemicals to extinguish small fires 24*

flashover: *arcing (sparking) across insulators caused by overvoltage on transmission lines 100*

flux linkages: *the linking of a magnetic field with the conductors of a coil when the magnetic field passes through the loops of the coil 149*

force: *a push or pull on an object with mass that causes it to change velocity 144*

fossil fuels: *natural energy sources (fuels) that formed in the earth over a very long period of time from the remains of ancient decomposed life forms (plants and animals) 159*

frame connection: *term used in structural steel engineering showing a simple connection made to a steel member 107*

friction: *the resistance that one surface experiences when moving over another 44*

fuel cell: *cell in which hydrogen-rich fuel is converted into clean electricity through a chemical reaction 160*

fuse: *safety device in an electric plug or circuit containing a thin wire that melts and breaks to stop the flow of current in case of a fault; cannot be reused 14*

galvanometer: *an instrument for detecting and measuring small electric currents 107*

gang lock: *a locking mechanism that allows many people to use their own padlocks to lock the mechanism; the locking mechanism can be removed only after each person has removed his/her padlock 13*

generator: *a machine that converts one form of energy into another, especially mechanical energy into electrical energy 44*

geothermal: *produced by the internal heat of the earth 160*

geyser: *domestic gas or electric water heater with a storage tank 114*

glacier: *a very large body of ice which moves very slowly 163*

glazing: *adding a layer of glass to porcelain using very high temperatures 100*

global warming: *a gradual increase in the average temperature of the earth's atmosphere as a result of the greenhouse effect 163*

gouges: *chisels with a concave blade used in carpentry 36*

greenhouse effect: *a process that occurs when gases in the earth's atmosphere trap the sun's heat 160*

greenhouse gases: *gases which have the ability to absorb infrared radiation (infrared light) emitted from the earth's surface and to radiate it back to the earth's surface 159, 160*

grinding wheel: *a wheel or disk made of abrasive material used in grinding machines for cutting or smoothing hard materials 36*

hazard: *source of exposure to danger 3*

horseplay: *rough play; fooling around 9*

hurricane: *large, rotating tropical storm with high winds and heavy rain 163*

hygroscopic: *tending to absorb moisture from the environment 101*

IEC: *International Electrotechnical Commission, the body responsible for recommending internationally accepted symbols and units 46*

ignite: *catch fire 23*

inadvertent: *not resulting from or achieved through deliberate planning 112*

incandescent: *producing light as a result of heat 45*

incident: *something that happened; an event or occurrence 4*

infinity (∞): *larger than any number 147*

infrared radiation: *electromagnetic radiation that is invisible to the human eye but can be felt as heat; also called infrared light 159*

installation (electrical): *an assembly of electrical wiring, electrical components and outlets in a residential, commercial or industrial setting 12*

insulation resistance tester: *measuring instrument designed to measure the resistance of insulators; also called a megaohmmeter 128*

insulator: *any substance that does not allow electrons to move easily from one atom to another when a potential difference is applied across this substance 46, 99*

interlock switch: *switch used to prevent incorrect operation by interrupting or diverting current from one conductor to another 14*

internal resistance: *the resistance of the internal components of a cell or battery 84*

internal voltage drop: *decrease in electrical potential caused by the current flowing through the internal components of a battery 84*

inversely proportional: *the bigger one value, the smaller another value; for example, the bigger the resistance, the smaller the current (Ohm's law) 46*

isolate: *to open or break a circuit so that it is not electrically continuous (i.e. so that current cannot flow) 12*

isolator: *device used for isolating a circuit or equipment from a source of power; also called a disconnector 12*

kinetic energy: *energy possessed by a body because of its motion 160*

leakage current: *electric current that has crossed a boundary normally viewed as insulating 15*

lessor: *a person who leases or lets a property to another; a landlord 127*

light-emitting diode (LED): *a semiconductor light source that emits light when a current flows through it 96*

links: *associates 151*

live conductor: *conductor carrying current from the point of supply to the point of consumption 110*

load: *an electrical component or portion of a circuit that consumes electrical power 56*

lock-out switch: *manually operated disconnector with a locking facility 12*

lodestone: *a naturally magnetised mineral that can be used as a magnet 139*

lug: *used to terminate a conductor onto a stud or bolt 31*

luminaire: *a complete lighting unit consisting of one or more electric lamps with all of the necessary parts and wiring 116*

machine guard: *a protective device (shield, barrier or other protective system) that protects users from the hazardous parts of a machine 7*

magnetic field: *area or region around a magnet in which magnetic forces can be observed 138*

magnetic flux: *a measurement of the total magnetic field which passes through a given surface 138*

magnetic flux density: *the amount of magnetic flux (ϕ) passing through a specific area 143*

magnetic lines of flux (or magnetic field lines): *a visual tool used to represent the magnetic fields that are found around any magnet 138*

magnetism: *the attractive or repulsive forces exerted by magnets 138*

malleable: *can be hammered or pressed into shape without breaking or cracking 96*

Megger: *commercial name of an insulation resistance tester 129*

meter (electrical): *device that measures the amount of electrical energy consumed by a residence or business 109*

mica: *a silicate mineral found in granite and other rocks that is used as a thermal or electrical insulator 46*

misnomer: *a word or concept suggesting a meaning that is known to be wrong 44*

mnemonic: *memory aid 25*

motor: *a machine that uses electricity or fuel to produce movement 15*

multimeter: *a measuring instrument that can measure more than one electrical quantity 129*

mutual inductance: *ability of one coil (or circuit) to induce an emf in another coil because of a changing magnetic flux in the first coil 152*

near miss: *an undesired and unplanned event that does not result in personal injury, but may result in damage to property and/or business interruption 4*

neutral bar: *copper bar in the distribution board to which all neutral conductors are connected 110*

neutral conductor: *conductor returning current from the point of consumption to the point of supply 110*

neutron: *particle with no electrical charge 42*

nucleus: *the centre of an atom that is made up of protons and neutrons 42*

ohmmeter: *an instrument used for measuring electrical resistances in ohms (Ω) 107*

open circuit: *an incomplete electrical connection through which current cannot flow 44*

oppose: *to resist change; work against 42, 151*

orbital: *the path followed by an electron around the nucleus of an atom 42*

overcurrent: *any current load greater than that intended for the conductor 14*

overload: *a fault condition that occurs when the circuit is expected to carry more current than it was designed for 14*

overload relay: *a protective device used in motor circuits to automatically disconnect the motor from the supply in the event of any overcurrent 15*

pathogen: *small organism, such as a virus, bacterium or fungus, that can cause disease 163*

permeability: *the ability to support the formation of magnetic fields 140*

personal protective equipment: *any clothing and equipment intended to protect a worker's body from injury or infection 16*

pest: *insect or small animal that damages crops or food supplies 163*

photovoltaic: *able to produce electricity from light 160*

plant: *a building where goods are manufactured by machines 3*

plant housekeeping: *to have 'a place for everything and everything in its place' at all times 6*

pneumatic: *operated by gas or compressed air 32*

pneumatic tool: *a power tool that is powered by compressed air supplied by an air compressor; also called air tools 33*

point of consumption: *the point in any electrical installation where electrical energy is converted into another form of energy 121*

polarised capacitor: *a capacitor with an anode (+) and a cathode (–) 107*

pollution: *the presence or introduction of a harmful or poisonous substance into the environment 159*

polymer: *chemical compound with molecules bonded together in long, repeating chains 101*

potential difference: *the work done when 1 coulomb of charge is moved from one point to the other between two points in a circuit 43*

potential energy: *energy possessed by a body because of its position relative to another body 160*

power: *the rate at which work is done or the rate at which energy is consumed 49*

power rating (bulb): *the amount of electrical energy that a bulb will convert into light and heat energy in 1 second 49*

power tool: *a tool that requires an additional power source over and above manual labour 32*

primary cell: *an energy storage device that creates current flow in a circuit by an irreversible chemical reaction 80*

prime mover: *a natural or mechanical source of angular motion 158*

proton: *positive-charge carrier 42*

PVC: *polyvinyl chloride 46*

radiant: *sending out light; shining or glowing brightly 44*

renewable energy: *energy that is produced by renewable resources which can be used repeatedly (they are not depleted) or are replenished naturally 159*

replenish: *to fill up or make complete again 159*

resin: *synthetic organic polymer used as the basis of plastics, adhesives, varnishes, or other products 101*

resistance: *the opposition that a substance offers to the flow of electric current 45*

resistive circuit: *any circuit containing resistance only 46*

resistivity: *the resistance between the opposite faces of a 1 metre cube of that material; i.e. the resistance to current flow offered by a conductor because of the type of material it is made of; also called specific resistance 71, 74*

resistor: *an electrical component that limits or regulates the flow of electric current in an electric circuit 46*

respiratory system: *organs in the body that allow a person to breath 17*

rice paddy: *a field planted with rice growing in water 163*

safety: *a condition of being protected from danger, risk or harm, or being unlikely to cause danger, risk or harm 2*

safety switch: *a protective device used to protect electrical equipment from damage and people from injury by making and breaking electrical connections during everyday use 14*

sanitary: *clean and hygienic 6*

secondary cell: *an energy storage device that creates current flow in a circuit by a reversible chemical reaction 82*

self-inductance: *the property of an electric circuit or coil that causes an emf to be generated within itself as a result of a changing current 151*

semiconductor: *a solid substance that has a conductivity between that of an insulator and that of a conductor 46, 103*

short circuit: *a fault condition that occurs when an abnormal connection allows current to flow through an unintended path that has no or very little resistance 14*

single-phase: *a supply (system) having only one live conductor 108*

single-pole switch: *a switch that has only one set of contacts 127*

socket outlet: *a device that has two or more metallic spring contacts designed to accept the corresponding pins of a plug; designed for fixing onto or into a building element or other flat surface; arranged for connection to the wiring of an installation 115*

solar energy: *radiant energy emitted by the sun 44*

solder: *join to another substance using a filler substance with a lower melting point (called solder) 96*

solenoid: *a coil of wire that acts like a magnet when carrying current 140*

statically induced emf: *no physical motion is required to induce an emf; emf is induced by a changing magnetic field 151*

subcircuit: *a distinct circuit of an electrical installation 106*

switch: *device that controls the flow of current by making or breaking the flow of current 116*

switch disconnector: *an on-load isolator used to make, carry and break current flow under normal circuit conditions 107*

symbolic safety signs: *a type of sign that uses shape, colour and pictograms; displayed to ensure the safety of employees and visitors in a workplace 10*

temperature coefficient of resistance: *the increase or decrease in resistance per ohm original resistance per degree rise in temperature 77*

tensile strength: *ability of a material to withstand being stretch or pulled without breaking 98*

terminal voltage: *potential difference between the terminals of a cell when current flows 43*

thermal: *relating to heat 158*

thermostat: *device that regulates the temperature in a heating device 114*

tinned: *copper conductors are coated with a thin layer of tin to reduce oxidation and increase their lifespan 102*

tool: *a device, especially one held in the hand, used to carry out a particular function 29*

transient: *lasting only for a short time 123*

transistor: *a semiconductor device that regulates current flow and acts as an amplifier or a switch 103*

transmission line: *a system of conductors that transfers electrical power from generating plants to the substations that deliver power to customers 108*

transmission machine: *a machine that uses gears to transfer energy 8*

tungsten: *a dense, greyish white metal with a high melting point; also called wolfram 45*

turbine: *a rotary mechanical device 158*

unsafe act: *any act that is not performed according to prescribed safety standards or practice 5*

unsafe condition: *any deviation from accepted safety standards which, if not rectified, may be the cause of accidents resulting in injury and/or damage 5*

valence electron: *electron in the outermost orbital of an atom 42*

variable capacitor: *a capacitor with an anode (+) and a cathode (–) 107*

vector: *a quantity that has both direction and magnitude 139*

voltage drop: *the decrease of electrical potential along the path of a current flowing in an electric circuit 46*

voltmeter: *an instrument used for measuring electrical potential difference between two points in an electric circuit in volts (V) 107*

vulcanising: *hardening by treating with sulphur at a high temperature 102*

wildfire: *large, destructive fire in a wild area such as a bush, forest or grassland 163*

winding: *one or more turns of wire forming a continuous coil through which an electric current can pass 79*

wiring diagram: *a line drawing showing how the electrical wiring and components of an electrical installation should be connected 106*

Class tests

Important

These two class tests have been set assuming that 30% of the curriculum has been taught prior to Test 1 and the remaining 70% has been taught prior to Test 2. So, these two class tests provide practice questions for all modules. The practice exam, which follows after the two class tests, is set on 100% of the curriculum.

Test 1

DURATION: 1 HOUR **TOTAL MARKS: 35**

INSTRUCTIONS AND INFORMATION

1. Answer all the questions.
2. Read all the questions carefully.
3. Number the answers according to the numbering system used in this question paper.
4. Start each new question on a new page.
5. Use only a black or blue pen.
6. Write neatly and legibly.
7. Approximate all answers correct to the three decimal places.
8. All sketches and circuit diagrams must be large and fully labelled.

QUESTION 1: Safety precautions

1.1 What is an accident? (3)

1.2 State two unsafe acts that cause accidents or incidents in the workplace. (2)

1.3 What does plant housekeeping mean? (3)

1.4 State the function of an interlock switch. (2)

[10]

QUESTION 2: Fire and fire fighting

2.1 Name the three elements needed to sustain a fire. (3)

2.2 Name two types of fuels that form part of a Class B fire. (2)

[5]

QUESTION 3: Hand and power tools

3.1 Name the tools that you would use to perform the following functions:

3.1.1 Bend metal conduit pipes.

3.1.2 Remove the outer and inner sheaths of a cable. (2 × 1 = 2)

3.2 Identify the following tools:

3.2.1

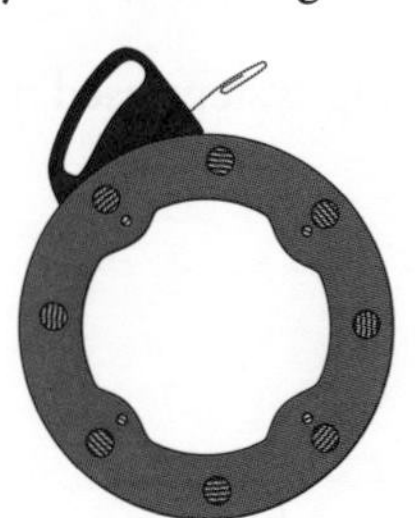

Figure 1

3.2.2

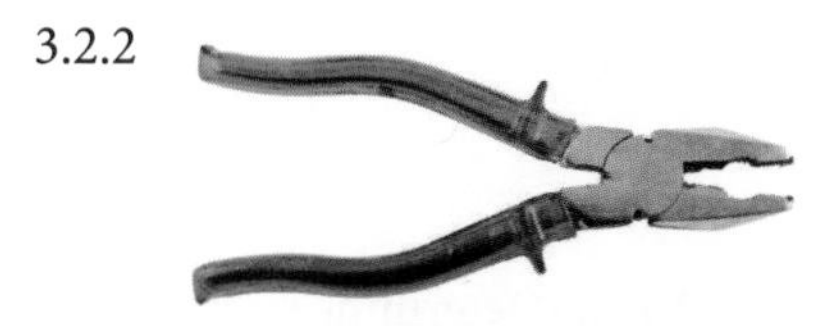

Figure 2

(2 × 1 = 2)

3.3 State one reason why it is important to care for and maintain power tools. (1)

[5]

QUESTION 4: Direct current circuit theory

4.1 Explain the difference between emf and potential difference. (4)

4.2 A farmer has twelve 250 W security lights around his property. The farm has a 240 V supply. Calculate:

4.2.1 The current drawn by each bulb. (2)

4.2.2 The resistance of each bulb's element. (2)

4.2.3 The energy dissipated by each bulb in 30 minutes. (2)

4.2.4 The cost to operate all of these security lights, if they operate for 9 hours per night and 30 nights per month. Take the cost of energy to be 185c/kWh. (5)

[15]

TOTAL: [35]

Test 2

DURATION: 2 HOURS **TOTAL MARKS: 70**

INSTRUCTIONS AND INFORMATION

1. Answer all the questions
2. Read all the questions carefully.
3. Number the answers according to the numbering system used in this questions paper.
4. Start each new question on a new page.
5. Use only a black or blue pen.
6. Write neatly and legibly.
7. Approximate all answers correct to three decimal places.
8. All sketches and circuit diagrams must be large and fully labelled.

QUESTION 1: Direct current theory

1.1 State Ohm's law. (3)

1.2 A coil of wire has a resistance of 36 Ω at 55 °C. Determine by how much the resistance will decrease if the coil is cooled to 0 °C. Take the temperature coefficient of resistance to be 0,004/°C at 0 °C. (3)

1.3 Two resistors of 8 Ω and 14 Ω are connected in series. This series combination is supplied by a battery with four identical cells in series. Each cell has an internal resistance of 0,2 Ω and an emf of 2,1 V. Calculate:

1.3.1 The total external resistance of the circuit. (2)

1.3.2 The total emf of the battery. (2)

1.3.3 The total current supplied by the battery. (4)

1.3.4 The potential difference of the battery. (2)

1.4 The flow of electrical current produces four effects. Name these effects. (4)

[20]

QUESTION 2: Conductors and insulating materials

2.1 What is a conductor? (2)

2.2 State one application of mica. (1)

2.3 What are semiconductors? (2)

[5]

QUESTION 3: Wiring of premises

3.1 Name three methods used by the supply authority to supply electrical energy to electrical installations. (3)

3.2 Name three places where a distribution board shall not be mounted unless it conforms to certain standards. (3)

3.3 Draw a neat and fully labelled sketch of a two-way switching circuit used to control three lights. (6)

3.4 State the function of lightning arrestors. (3)

3.5 What does the code of practice state with regards to earth leakage protection for socket outlets. (2)

3.6 Draw a neat and fully labelled circuit diagram of a geyser sub-circuit. (8)

[25]

QUESTION 4: Testing a single-phase installation

4.1 State the purpose of the earth and bonding continuity test. (2)

4.2 What is the minimum allowable reading when conducting the insulation resistance test? (1)

4.3 Name two instruments that can be used to conduct the polarity test. (2)

[5]

QUESTION 5: Magnetism and electromagnetism

5.1 State three properties of magnetic field lines. (3)

5.2 State Faraday's first law of electromagnetic induction. (3)

5.3 State two uses of electromagnetics. (2)

5.4 What do you understand by alternating current? (2)

[10]

QUESTION 6: Renewable energy

6.1 What do you understand by renewable energy? (3)

6.2 State two benefits of renewable energy. (2)

[5]

TOTAL: [70]

Practice exam

DURATION: 3 HOURS **TOTAL MARKS: 100**

INSTRUCTIONS AND INFORMATION

1. Answer all the questions.
2. Read all the questions carefully.
3. Number the answers according to the numbering system used in this questions paper.
4. Start each new question on a new page.
5. Use only a black or blue pen.
6. Write neatly and legibly.
7. Approximate all answers correct to three decimal places.
8. All sketches and circuit diagrams must be large and fully labelled.

QUESTION 1: Safety precautions

1.1 State two duties of an employer as given in the OHS Act. (2)

1.2 State two disadvantages of poor plant housekeeping. (2)

1.3 Symbolic safety signs consist of three parts. Name these parts. (3)

1.4 Name three types of gloves that are used for hand protection. (3)

[10]

QUESTION 2: Fire and firefighting

2.1 Name two types of fuels that contribute to a Class A fire. (2)

2.2 State two safety precautions to be observed in the event of a fire. (2)

2.3 Name one type of fire extinguisher used in a Class C fire. (1)

[5]

QUESTION 3: Hand and power tools

3.1 State three aspects concerning the care and maintenance of hand tools. (3)

3.2 Name any two power sources needed to operate a power tool. (2)

[5]

QUESTION 4: Direct current circuit theory

4.1 State the four factors that affect the resistance of a conductor. (4)

4.2 A copper conductor has a length of 1,25 km and a resistance of 4,75 Ω.

Calculate the diameter of the conductor if its resistivity is 0,027 μΩ m. (6)

4.3 Define temperature coefficient of resistance. (3)

4.4 State what happens to the resistance of the following materials when their temperature increases:

4.4.1 Nichrome.

4.4.2 Copper.

4.4.3 Carbon. (3 × 1 = 3)

4.5 A 20 Ω resistor is connected in series with a 45 Ω resistor. This series combination is then connected in parallel with an 18 Ω resistor. The circuit is supplied at 75 V.

Draw a large and fully labelled circuit diagram and then calculate:

4.5.1 The total resistance of the circuit. (3)

4.5.2 The total current drawn from the supply. (2)

4.5.3 The current drawn by each resistor. (3)

4.5.4 The voltage drop across each resistor. (3)

4.5.5 The energy dissipated by the circuit in 2,5 minutes. Express your answer in kJ. (3)

[30]

QUESTION 5: Conductor and insulating materials

5.1 Which is the best known conductor? (1)

5.2 State two uses of hard-drawn copper in the electrical field. (2)

5.3 State the function of insulators. (2)

[5]

QUESTION 6: Wiring of premises

6.1 Draw the IEC wiring symbols for the following:

6.1.1 Coil.

6.1.2 Earth connection.

6.1.3 Switch disconnector. (3)

6.2 Fill in the missing words in the following regulation.

A distribution board is an _____ that contains electrical _____ for the _____ or control of electrical power from one or more incoming circuits to one or more _____. (4)

6.3 Make a neat and fully labelled sketch to show the internal wiring of a distribution board in which the ELR is used as the main-switch disconnector. (8)

6.4 What does the code of practice state with regards to earth leakage protection for geysers? (3)

6.5 Name three practical examples where two-way switching will be needed. (3)

6.6 Copy the following table into your answer book and complete it:

Sub-circuit	Size of circuit breaker	Size of conductor
Geyser		
Lights		

(4)

[25]

QUESTION 7: Testing of a single-phase installation

7.1 A registered person can issue a certificate of compliance. State the two things that must be done prior to the certificate being issued. (2)

7.2 Name the instrument used to conduct the insulation resistance test. (1)

7.3 State the function of the polarity test. (2)

[5]

QUESTION 8: Magnetism and electromagnetism

8.1 What does exciting or energising a coil mean? (2)

8.2 What do you understand by mutual inductance? (3)

8.3 Name two types of statically induced emfs. (2)

8.4 State three methods that can be used to increase the strength of the magnetic field around a solenoid. (3)

[10]

QUESTION 9: Renewable energy

9.1 Name three types of renewable energy. (3)

9.2 Name two human activities that increase greenhouse gases. (2)

[5]

TOTAL: [100]